The Other Side of the Coin

The Other Side of the Coin

by

Juan M. Isais

Translated from Spanish by

Elisabeth F. Isais

William B. Eerdmans Publishing Company
Grand Rapids, Michigan

Printed in the United States of America.
Library of Congress Catalog Card Number: 66-18721

First printing, March 1966
Second printing, November 1967

PHOTOLITHOPRINTED BY CUSHING - MALLOY, INC.
ANN ARBOR, MICHIGAN, UNITED STATES OF AMERICA
1967

Dedication

To my beloved friend and companion in evangelism,
the late Dr. R. Kenneth Strachan,
a man with an old message and a contemporary mind;

to the general director of Christian Service Fellowship,
the Rev. Spencer Bower, who believed wholeheartedly
in the ideas expressed in this book and encouraged me
to go ahead;

and to all those who consciously or unconsciously
provided the material on which the story is based;

and to my beloved wife, who not only spent many hours
translating the manuscript, but also gave me her
professional help on more than one occasion.

Preface

Out of years of active service for the Saviour in Latin America and widespread evangelistic ministry, there comes this thoughtful and very helpful analysis of gospel work in that area, with a carefully considered and constructive consideration for the future of gospel ministry in Latin-American lands. There is a perspective that gives understanding of the past and present status of missions, with penetrating insight into the problems faced by missionaries, national pastors and the indigenous church. Above all, the analysis shows deep appreciation for the missionary work and awareness of the perplexities that must be faced in these years of transition.

There is need for communication among the missionaries themselves, between the missionaries and the national pastors and their churches, and among the nationals themselves. Out of such communication, given in Christian love, courtesy and candor, there can come full understanding of one another. The call is for prayer, for planning, for a positive program that meets the problems and opportunities of today, and all this can be done in the power of the Holy Spirit.

All this is done in story form, which makes for pleasant reading; yet it is also painful in its searching analysis of every believing heart, both missionary and national. It is to be read prayerfully, patiently, personally.

DR. V. RAYMOND EDMAN
Chancellor of Wheaton College
Former Missionary to Ecuador

Introduction

In a dramatic, and perhaps to some a shocking, manner, Juan Isais has painted a vivid picture of a number of the basic tensions which lie beneath the surface of so many interpersonal relationships between missionaries and nationals in Latin America. He has indicated clearly how failure to understand the Latin's concept of time, courtesy, and personal friendship can be devastating to many aspects of effective missionary work and how the proper exposure of misunderstanding can be spiritually healthy and organizationally significant.

The author of this very readable book is well-equipped to deal with these problems, for he has had years of experience with missions and churches in Latin America, working intimately with numerous organizations and discovering in his day-to-day contacts some of the fundamental problems which tend to be so injurious to the cause of Christ. Moreover, his approach represents sound anthropology, though it does not go by this name.

Quite naturally Juan Isais' purpose is mutual understanding, but he has written here primarily to help us see ourselves as Latins see us, with our pre-occupations for schedules, organizational efficiency, and programs, rather than people. Rather than tell us this outright, he has portrayed us in story form, at times in none-too-pleasing roles, in order that we might become more aware of our shortcomings.

Like any artist, Juan Isais has been obliged to select his colors and structure his composition, not with the sociologist's eye to statistical or photographic detail, but with the painter's sense of relevant highlighting, for in somber statistical treatments the important personal factors are too often overlooked. In order to deal with essentially human factors, the author has chosen the most popular of literary forms — the story. It is evident that in such a presentation, Juan Isais would not claim that these are the precise problems which one meets on all fields or that they attain the same degree of intensity in all missions. What he is trying to say is that they are typical, and as such can be expected wherever Latins and Anglo-Saxons work together. It is out of these basic differences of personality that misunderstandings arise, and their elimination requires frank recognition and spiritual empathy.

As a book addressed primarily to missionaries, it should certainly be read by all candidates before going out, but it will probably be more fully appreciated and understood by those who have had several years' experience in the field, for only then can one see himself against the background of Latin life.

It is to be hoped that this book can be followed by another, which will treat the ways in which nationals and missionaries can work creatively together, once they have benefitted from a mutual recognition of their personality differences and faults. This acceptance in love and dedication to the common task is ultimately the goal for which we all pray and toward which we all strive, but as a first step in this direction Juan Isais has given us a well-written and penetrating analysis.

DR. EUGENE A. NIDA
Translations Secretary
American Bible Society

Contents

Chapter One

The Word Was Made Flesh

It is one o'clock on a Saturday afternoon. A soft breeze is blowing and the office is pleasantly cool, but Louis Smith, a middle-aged, pleasant-faced man with dark-rimmed glasses, is quite oblivious to his surroundings. In recent days he has been suffering increasingly from a strange frustration, a gnawing feeling that possibly all his years of missionary service have not produced everything they should have. The same doubts have been worrying his attractive wife Lila, who with him has become concerned over the fact that their long hours of prayer and careful planning and work have resulted in such a small number of converts. What has gone wrong with all their well-intentioned efforts? Louis, slumped in front of the old roll-top desk, with his hands behind his head, is not sure.

He is a man who loves God; it was that love which prompted him to leave his homeland and make his home in a foreign country. But this afternoon he is disheartened. His seemingly tireless service for Christ has not succeeded in imparting a like vision to the national leaders under his care, either in the spiritual or the material realm. But why? Unable to contain his thoughts any longer, Louis puts a sheet of paper into the typewriter and begins to bang away:

Dear Jim:

How are you doing? I hope everything is fine.

Lately I've been wanting to write you — and I hope you won't be too surprised or disillusioned at what I'm going to say — but I feel you are the only friend to whom I dare pour out my inmost thoughts and perhaps clear up my own thinking a bit. As you know, I've been living in this country for many years, and as far as I know, I've been faithful in praying for these people, although I suppose I should have been more persistent. I can't deny that God has done some marvellous things — I think I told you about Julio, the atheist who was so miraculously converted to the Lord, and maybe you remember about fifteen years ago when I wrote you about Margarita? Well, since then she has grown and progressed steadily, and even though her parents are dirt-poor and illiterate, Margarita is now a fine school teacher.

Not to bore you, but I think too that all the children — to avoid exaggeration, let's say fifty percent of them — that Lila had in her Bible club when we began our missionary work here have continued in the faith. So in general I suppose I have no complaints.

But frankly, my problem is that I'm not at all sure my ministry has been successful, either for my own personal satisfaction or for the Lord. In spite of all my efforts to educate these people, buy clothes for them, give them spiritual orientation, and so on, I don't feel they either like me or appreciate me. Something is wrong somewhere, and I'm almost tempted to feel that the fault is theirs, because as far as I'm concerned, what more love could I have shown them? After all, here I am living in a strange country, staying year after year to help them in spite of the poor health conditions, barely adequate income, ingratitude of the people, and all the offenses I've had to put up with!

Lately I've come to the conclusion that no matter how much we do for these people, they will never develop beyond a certain level of spiritual intelligence. Maybe that's why Pedro has never paid me back the ten dollars he borrowed eight years ago, etc. And even though I've invited many of the brethren from the church to come to the house here, they don't seem to feel free to drop in as though we were truly their friends. By the same token, we don't go to their homes either, at least not just as friends.

Well, Jim, don't misunderstand — I'm not totally discouraged. The work is the Lord's. But this situation does bother me, and I just felt that I had to share it with someone to get it out of my system. Forgive me for making you my scapegoat! Any advice will be cheerfully accepted. Maybe you can see some of the flaws in my train of thought. . . .

Lila is fine, and the children too. We've sent them to school in Tiquistlan, where we have a beautiful farm and the missionary children can learn without having to mix with the natives. There's no denying the fact that the local customs are odd, to say the least, and we also want to avoid any possibility that Mary might get interested in one of the boys from church here. You know how unfortunate that could be.

Peter is developing very nicely. Imagine, he wants to be a missionary! But with this anti-missionary spirit that seems so strong around here lately, I think he'd almost better go into some other calling, or at least into a different part of the world. After all is said and done, we've already helped the work here enough, and it's time they learned to stand on their own two feet. Probably I told you that the Board has decided to cut down on its financial help and the churches will soon have to be fully self-supporting. Sometimes I think we should follow the example of other boards who have removed their support without such a long warning period, but I suppose that wouldn't be too wise either.

Let me know how your family is doing, what's new in the church, and your plans for vacation, etc. Who knows — we might see each other sooner than we had planned.

Your friend in Christ,
Louis

Louis had not finished addressing the envelope when Lila burst in, as usual looking lovely as a dark-haired beauty queen to his prejudiced eyes, all excited now because she had just come across a Scripture verse which had suddenly taken on new meaning for her. Her husband leaned back, put one foot on the desk, and grinned, "Well, good for you — my congratulations. But you haven't told me which verse it is."

With a satisfied smile, Lila bent over to show him her Bible. "Look, here it is — I've underlined it. 'And the Word was made flesh, and dwelt among us.' Do you see? Jesus *dwelt* among us!"

"But what on earth is so new about that? I've known that verse since I was a child. It simply means that Christ, being God, came in human flesh to live among men. Granted it is a tremendous truth, but not too original at this point."

"But that's exactly it — Christ did it in such a way that we understand what He did for us and we appreciate it, don't you see?"

"Well, I'd say your theology is pretty elementary, but congratulations anyway — I can see that it's been a blessing to you. By the way, I just wrote a letter to Jim. Want to read it before it's mailed?"

Lila took off her apron and sat down to read. Louis, meanwhile, left to change clothes for his regular Saturday afternoon trip to the Club. The members, mostly from the upper class, liked to save their Saturdays for recreation and Louis was a faithful participant in their sports activities. Most missionaries did not belong, but because Louis's work was so largely administrative, it helped take his mind off other matters.

When he had dressed he returned to the office, but Lila was still reading his letter, so he told her hastily, "Dear, when you are finished, send the letter to the post office, okay? And if Manuel comes looking for me, tell him I'll be glad to help him with that problem, but to let me know ahead of time. Maybe we can make an appointment for next week. See you later, dear."

Louis hurried out of the house and as he was opening the car door he saw Leonardo, pastor of one of the churches, walking toward him. When Leonardo realized that the missionary was about to leave, he hastened his steps. It was obvious that Louis was not on his way to work, since his flowered shirt and informal slacks gave an immediate clue as to his destination.

Although he was already a few minutes late, Louis called as cordially as possible, "Hello, Leonardo! What can I do for you? Sorry I'm in a bit of a hurry right now."

"Well, don Louis, as a matter of fact I did come to ask a favor of you. The church is having a big visitation campaign, trying to reach our entire area house-to-house, and. . . ."

"Wonderful! That's exactly what we missionaries like to see."

Leonardo looked startled. "What do you mean?"

"Why, we like to see folks taking initiative and taking on the responsibility for projects like this. Congratulations. I trust the Lord will give you much fruit from your campaigns. When are you planning to start?" Louis half expected Leonardo to say "tomorrow," since he had a rather cynical attitude toward the haphazard way these national pastors usually planned things. But he was completely taken aback by Leonardo's reply:

"We're starting right away, within the hour. We planned it all on Thursday night. The whole church is supposed to meet at three o'clock for prayer and then go out two by two. That's why I came, so I could ask you to help me visit the street where upper class people like the Ferrers and Goyas live — I just don't feel capable of calling on them without you. Could you come with me right away, or perhaps drive over in a few minutes?"

Louis was not sure whether to laugh or cry. For months he had been talking about the need for a house-to-house visitation campaign, without any response, and now all of a sudden the church was starting out, with practically no publicity, he supposed, no prayer, no planning . . . probably not even any attractive literature to give out. He felt more discouraged than ever. Furthermore, for him to refuse to help would seem a selfish thing to do, especially when Leonardo could easily see that he was on his way to the Club. Why hadn't he left home a few minutes earlier and avoided Leonardo entirely? Better yet, why not just give up missionary work altogether, instead of trying to get along with these impossible people?

He must give Leonardo some kind of an answer. "My, but I wish you had asked me sooner! I've promised to go somewhere else this afternoon. You know how we gringos are — tied down to our date books, our clocks, our schedules, and all that sort of thing. But I'll tell you what. If you decide to organize another visitation campaign, let me know, and I'll go with you with much pleasure. Forgive me . . . but next time ask me sooner!"

Leonardo did not press further, but said good-bye and turned to start the long walk back. He was accustomed to walking and thought little of hiking the twenty blocks which separated the missionary's home from the church. When he reached the corner, Louis passed him and waved, but it was evident from the sound of the motor that he was in a hurry — he had promised to meet his partners at 2:30.

"And now," thought Leonardo, "how am I going to go about organizing my people? I'd been counting on don Louis, but . . . I might have known. I should have asked him yesterday. He's always telling me to let him know in advance when

I need his help. Well, there's no choice now but to go ahead. We're on the horse and have to ride it."

When he arrived, somewhat out of breath, he found a good number of church officers ready to go out on the visitation, although most of the membership was conspicuous by its absence. Leonardo assigned each person a section to visit, with the help of a city map brought in for the purpose, and carefully explained that he and Louis would take care of the street where the upper class people lived. "Don Louis couldn't make it this afternoon because he had a very important appointment that had been made a long time ago," Leonardo explained in an exaggerated effort to gloss over the missionary's absence, "but he and I will be responsible for this section" — pointing to the area on the map. And without more ado, the small nucleus of church workers departed to carry out their evangelistic task.

Meanwhile, back at the Smith home, Lila still sat thinking about her husband's letter to Jim. The more she thought, the more she disagreed. "How can it be," she asked herself dejectedly, "that we have spent so many years on the mission field and yet so little has been accomplished? I'm afraid something is wrong. In fact, I'm sure of it — this verse in John is so clear to me now — Christ voluntarily left the glory of heaven and descended all the way down to our level. Hmm! I wonder how much we really think and feel like these people here, on *their* level. Sometimes we worry about how the people do or don't appreciate us, more than we worry about their growth in Christ. And yet we are concerned about that, too. . . ."

She straightened up. "Oh dear, I wish I knew what it is that is troubling us lately. Maybe it's just the doldrums of our mid-forties, and yet I think perhaps the Lord is trying to teach us something new that we need to learn. At least I know this much — in spite of everything, I for one am not in favor of giving up and going home just because we feel a little frustrated right now!"

Reaching out for a sheet of paper, she chewed a pencil for a moment and then wrote with firm strokes, "Something has to be done soon. Something *must* be done soon. The hope of tomorrow is the reality with which we face our problems today."

She held the paper for a moment, a slight frown on her brow, and then placed it carefully in the center of her husband's desk. That done, she went out to call Alejandro, the gardener and general handyman around the house, to take the letter to the post office before Louis should return.

That same evening, after their usual bedtime devotions, Louis and Lila began to talk again. "You know, Lila, before I went to church tonight I went by the office and saw that note you left me. In a way I suppose you are right, but I wonder if you really understand what is behind all this."

"What do you mean?"

"Well, I think the time of pioneer missionaries is passing. Even though we feel sad about it, we must insist that the nationals take the responsibility, and that we remove ourselves increasingly from the center of the picture."

"All right," agreed Lila, "but what are we doing to see that our pastors awaken to their responsibilities and develop a sense of independence in their work?"

Louis was too worn out to discuss the point. "Dear, the only way is to leave them alone. They will find the solution sooner or later. After all, maybe tomorrow we'll be asked to leave the country entirely; the communists might take over and then we couldn't do anything anyhow."

"But . . . until they do throw us out, don't you think we could be doing more than we are?"

"Well, look — I'm so tired that I can't think and anyhow it's time to sleep and not to make plans or discuss big ideas," yawned Louis. "If you want to, why don't you think of something to present at the annual meetings of the Mission?"

Lila brightened. "You're right. That's a marvellous idea.

You go to sleep — I want to stay up and think for a while longer."

While Louis turned over and closed his eyes, Lila got up and began to write down a long list of ideas and possibilities that could be presented to the Mission. For about two hours her thoughts roamed in different directions, eventually converging on a few major recommendations. She had no inkling of the results of that sleepless night — all she knew then was that it seemed to give some relief to the feelings of frustration she'd been suffering lately. When she finally went back to bed, sleep came more easily than it had in weeks.

Chapter Two

Transition

After a very busy Sunday, Louis was in the post office on Monday morning when he saw Theodore Allen, a young missionary from another Board. Ted was obviously rushed, but Louis's friendly smile obliged him to stop and chat a minute. "How's it going?" asked Louis, his hand on Ted's shoulder. "How's the work of your Mission these days?"

"Oh, all right, more or less."

"What do you mean?"

"Well, we're having some problems with the pastors. They simply do not want to produce what they should, and I have had to adjust myself to a program that is entirely too full."

"Have you learned to get up at four o'clock in the morning yet?" Louis queried with a meaningful smile.

"No, that's entirely too early — although the other day I had to do it because Ramon got it into his head. . . ."

"Who is Ramon?" interrupted Louis.

"Don't you know him? He's the pastor of the very first evangelical church that was founded here in the city." Ted seemed amazed that Louis had not had contact with such an important pastor. "Anyhow, imagine — the other day he got it into his head that we should distribute tracts to the workmen at four o'clock in the morning! But I just couldn't do it. My body is the Lord's and I can't mistreat it that much."

"You must have the same problem I do," agreed Louis. "No matter how early I begin the day, I'm always behind."

"Precisely. I get up at 6:30. At 7:00 I help my wife to get the children ready because the school bus picks them up at 7:30. Then I go to the market, even though I know the pastors hate to see me carrying a market basket, but you know we just can't trust our servants. Our cook is a believer, but somehow these people never seem to lose their bad habits, and anyhow it's better to buy according to your own tastes. Well, after that I have a time of personal devotions — I've promised the Lord I won't give in and begin my work until I have had a very intimate communion with Him. Then I come here to the post office, which takes me half an hour or so, although lately I've found a new route which saves a fifth of a mile. From here generally I go to the office, so whenever you want me, just come on over. I'm at your orders."

"That's a good idea," said Louis. "What about ten o'clock this morning — that's coffee time, isn't it?"

"Wonderful. It's almost that now. Where shall we meet?"

"I'll go to your office, if you'd like. I'm interested in talking to you some more about some of these problems we're all facing in the work."

"Of course. You'll always be welcome."

They shook hands according to the formal national custom which they had adopted as their own, and parted. Louis had no sooner reached his office at the Bible Institute than his telephone rang. It was Ted. "Listen, forgive me for bothering you so soon, but I want to ask your advice. A lady from the church is asking that I take her son to the hospital. Might I get into difficulties if I take a sick man in my car? Should I get some kind of special permission, or check first with the hospital, or what? I've never done it; that's why I sound so ignorant. I don't like to tangle with the authorities."

"Brother," replied Louis, "these people are opportunists; they'll always be bothering you for something. The same thing used to happen to me when I went to conferences. People began asking me to take them, and I used to help some of them out, but little by little they started taking advantage of me to the point that I had to make two or three trips to the Convention just to take pastors, wives, children, in-laws, and so on ad nauseum. So after my first term I promised myself I wouldn't take anyone in my car, and I even bought a little European model so I'd have less difficulties. I'd suggest you avoid the problem, Ted — do it tactfully, but do it now."

"But she's going to come here!" Ted sounded desperate.

"That's all right," answered Louis. "Just leave word that you are busy, or maybe the best thing is to tell her frankly that you can't help in a situation like this. Sometimes it's better to get it over with, once and for all."

"Well, the fact is that I do have a terrific amount of work to do today, and I shouldn't take the time to go. I think I'll leave right away and do some of my errands. My secretary can tell dona Maria I was busy. What do you say if I see you later in your office instead of having you come here?"

"Fine," answered Louis. "I'll be looking for you about 10:15."

Ted got up to leave the office, saying to his secretary in a confidential tone as he passed, "Tell Maria to forgive me — I have too much to do today and I can't help her out. If you think a letter from the Mission would help her, you may write one yourself. Okay?"

Without lifting her head from the stencil she was cutting, the secretary agreed to do all she could to comfort Maria. And Ted went out.

When the two men were together again, sipping hot coffee in a corner café, Louis began, "I just received a letter from out Stateside office telling me to take the necessary steps to reorganize our work here, so that the nationals can take over within the briefest possible time. It sounds a bit strange, but I'm thinking about it. At any rate, I must confess I'm upset — those men up there in the States don't know anything about our problems here, nor do they understand the people, because if they did they wouldn't issue such impractical orders. But anyhow, what do you think about these trends? What experience does your Mission have along this line?"

"Well," Ted smiled, "we're in the same boat. Of course, maybe you'll say I'm just too green myself, but to tell the truth I do believe that if the work is to progress, we should turn over the leadership to nationals. However, I'm frank to admit that it isn't going to be easy."

"So you really think a step like that is necessary?"

"Well, if you like, I'll expound on the subject a bit."

"Go ahead," replied Louis. "You know the old saying — when a man is willing to listen, he learns more than when he thinks about what he's going to say."

"Well, as I said, nothing we do will be easy, but one thing I have thought about is that we should open up this whole subject for discussion. For instance, we should discuss the problem in different Mission committees and see what recommendations our men come up with. Maybe they'd have some good ideas, and we should enlist their cooperation from the beginning anyhow."

Louis nodded. "Yes, one of our big problems is to get a feeling of unanimity among the missionaries about this thing."

Ted went on, "Another possibility — not as radical as you may think at first glance — would be to interview each of our pastors, one by one, to try to get an idea of what they think about the future of the work here. You know — informal, friendly interviews. And we might also ask the leaders of each church to prepare some kind of report for the Mission, giving us an idea of *their* feelings about this problem of national versus missionary leadership. I realize we haven't been accustomed to that type of approach, but perhaps the situation warrants it now."

Louis took a gulp of coffee and sighed. "You know, Ted, this thing is bigger than we are. I sometimes wonder if I have the spiritual strength I need to face the future as a missionary. Well, give me some more of your ideas!"

They continued discussing various possibilities until Louis finally called for the check from the waitress and said, "Well, I'm going to think about what you've said — you've probably got something there. It's a shame we have so many difficulties all the time, isn't it? We seem to spend more time and energy trying to find solutions than we do in moving ahead with the work of the Gospel." He paused. "Now if you'll excuse me, I'd better be getting home. I try to be on time for lunch every day, and no matter what, I've never been late yet — I think that's one way to avoid problems in the home. What would you say if we get together another day to talk some more? I think you've given me a lot of light." The two men shook hands and parted hastily.

Arriving home, Louis discovered that he still had five minutes before lunch, and so he eased down on the sofa, put his feet on the coffee table, and started to read the new *Time* magazine. For some reason the local newspaper was never to be found in the Smith home, suggesting that they had little interest in the country's internal problems. It was much easier to keep up on world affairs by reading *Time* each week in their own language, plus other magazines sent to them by loyal friends back home, although in case of a national emergency they usually bought a paper in the street just to keep up on the headlines.

But this noon Lila would not leave her husband in peace. "Louis, have you read that verse I showed you the other day?" He shook his head. "It's on my mind all the time and I'm convinced it means something special for us. Especially when I think of what you wrote to Jim, I feel *so* concerned, as if we need some new answer from the Lord." Her voice grew more urgent. "Don't you feel a bit uneasy these days, as though God had something to teach us?"

"Oh, I don't know — maybe you're right." Louis could see that Lila was much in earnest, and so after they were seated at the table and had given thanks he asked her to continue with her ideas. "What do you have in mind?"

"Well, I don't agree with what you wrote to Jim, for one thing. Your ideas are too extreme. The people here are intelligent and they're hungry for the Gospel. You can tell they're unhappy just by looking at the way they act. It seems to me that we ought to do something more than we have been doing, to help the work go forward."

"All right, Lila, I'm willing to listen. What do you think we ought to do and why do you keep insisting that we have to do something right away?" Louis took another helping of meat and potatoes. It was obvious that he wouldn't be able to take his usual quick nap after lunch, although fortunately everyone knew that he preferred not to be disturbed until two o'clock and so he and Lila could have a long conversation without interruptions. "Let's take all the time we need, Lila. I'm interested in your ideas and suggestions."

"Well, in the first place, it seems to me that as ambassadors of Christ we shouldn't expect people to appreciate us. That's the sort of thing the Bible attributes to publicans and sinners. I think the child of God has an even greater responsibility to preach the Word in the very places where he is least appreciated. After all, what makes our activity worthwhile is not the people's attitude toward *us,* but toward our message. We are here *because* we love the people, not *so* that they will love us."

"But Lila," interrupted Louis, "we are human beings of flesh and blood, and we need to have our emotional life revitalized with some gesture of gratitude and respect from others, don't we? Missionaries aren't so different from other people. I don't ask for anything from the non-Christians, but it's logical to expect that those who are our spiritual children should have some feeling of love for us . . . it seems to me."

"Yes, but you've just said it — we are human beings. The work we represent does have those limitations. Only by the mercy of God will we have the opportunity of receiving thanks from the people, but it is not something we should expect or demand. When we don't receive thanks, we shouldn't use that as a means of escape, either."

Louis wrinkled his forehead. "Explain yourself. If I recall correctly, you were pretty down in the mouth a week or so ago, about this very same problem."

"Well, that's true — I was pretty discouraged, but I think the Lord has helped me see where I was wrong. Now I realize that we are morally and spiritually obligated to see that the work goes forward, without hoping for payment from the brethren here, either in terms of appreciation or of understanding."

Louis apparently did not follow her reasoning. "All right, before you go off on another tangent, tell me one, two, three what you think we ought to do."

"My dear husband — it may surprise you, but I have something written down. Do you want to see it?"

"Of course," Louis said, getting up to reach for the sheet of paper Lila offered him. On it was written:

Suggestions for our next Mission meetings

I. Evaluation of our present-day methods compared with those used by the first missionaries.

II. Elaboration of plans that should bring better methods, etc., for the good of the work here in the country.

III. Exchange of ideas with the nationals in order to see what they think of us and of our methods of work.

IV. Immediate steps toward the independence of the national church in the fullest sense of the word, as our leaders up north have requested, on the basis of a just and reasonable plan.

As Louis read, he couldn't help remembering the conversation with Ted just an hour earlier. "Well, Lila, congratulations. These are good ideas — but do you think they are practical? When could we do these things?"

"Well, we could begin in the very next meeting that we have with the pastors and leaders. I think that instead of dedicating all the time to devotional messages as we usually do, we could include some frank, open discussions as well. We ought to seek for a mutual understanding of the goals that we *all* have, or should have, for the future of the work."

The more Louis thought about it, the more he felt that she was going too far. "Now, dear, they aren't going to understand all the implications of these things, beginning with this business of evaluation. Don't you know that these natives here never go anywhere on time? How can you really evaluate anything if you don't take the factor of time into consideration?"

"All right, you have a point, but they are the ones who should do the evaluating with us, not just we alone," insisted Lila a bit stubbornly.

Louis was beginning to feel bored with the discussion and decided to end it. "I think if we want to start off on the right track, Lila, we should present these ideas first to the Mission in our annual meeting, and *then* bring them to the national brethren. Don't you agree?"

Lila smiled. "Oh well, that was my original idea anyhow."

Thanks to Lila's initiative and persistence, the list of ideas actually was presented at the annual meeting. Unfortunately, however, it caused a hot discussion which practically divided the missionaries into two camps — one led by young Edward Edson, who had somewhat revolutionary ideas, and the other by Dr. Oliver Budd, a missionary with many years of experience. In general, the two groups tended to be made up according to the length of service of their members, although a few of the older ones lined up with Edward.

After the first meeting, Lila sought out Louis. "What do you think, dear, about Edward's position?"

"Bad, bad, bad," said Louis categorically. "These youngsters are always sticking their feet in their mouths. They are very idealistic but they don't know anything about either the culture or the people. Everything Edward says is impractical. I wish we'd never started all this."

Lila looked up at him. "Why, I thought Edward had some fairly good ideas. He has a very broad understanding of modern trends in missions — I think he's done a lot of studying on the subject. We ought to keep an open mind on these new ideas."

"My dear, sometimes you forget the experiences you've had. We certainly can't open the door to let nationals join the Mission on an equal basis with the rest of us, for instance, just to take one of his crazy ideas. In the first place, they don't have enough education. In the second place, they are completely irresponsible. Furthermore, we don't have funds to pay their salaries. And they are so pretentious that they'd probably want to earn the same as we do, even though they don't have the same needs." Louis shook his head and paused for breath. "This business of turning over the property is another mistake. The money is the Lord's, and we must take care of it. If we give them the title deeds to all the churches and parsonages, and I suppose they want the institutions too, they are quite capable of selling it all — and before long they won't have any church whatsoever, either physical or spiritual. No, no, I can't go along with that. At any rate, the legal arrangement would have to be very carefully worked out."

Lila listened, attentive and thoughtful.

"This business of increasing their income is almost impossible, too, for the simple reason that we don't have anything in the budget to cover it. The pastor's pay ought to come from the churches, and you know perfectly well that there is no hope on that score. Let's have them continue to earn twenty-five to forty dollars a month, and maybe over the years they can earn more when the churches become more conscious of their needs."

"Well, I think . . ." began Lila, a bit hesitantly, not wanting to antagonize Louis any further, "it seems to me that this business is going to come up again tomorrow, and I wish that you and I could contribute to its success. I don't know just how, but my heart cries out against the injustice that I'm beginning to believe exists. I really think we ought to give serious consideration to Edward's ideas."

Louis started to reply, but decided against it. He could see that Lila was distressed — better to drop the matter for the present. His own convictions had not changed in the least, although he resolved to be as open-minded as possible. After all, if the decisions were too radical for his taste, he could always stay home after his next furlough and take a teaching position!

Surprisingly enough, the final sessions of the meetings produced some real progress. According to the "liberal" party's viewpoint, the decisions left much to be desired, but . . . something was better than nothing. Tall, bespectacled Edward, who had suddenly been catapulted into a position of leadership, proposed the following:

1) We should invite our national brethren to attend the next Mission meeting, and tell us frankly what criticisms or suggestions they would make for the better progress of the work; then we should adopt energetic measures to do away with anything and everything which clouds our relationship with our brethren.

2) As foreigners, we should ask the Lord to take away our persecution complex, and to that end we should give up any activity which tends to separate us from our national brethren, until we become totally integrated, both spiritually and socially.

3) We should schedule orientation sessions in order to ex-

plain to the national leaders how the Mission works, both in the homeland and locally.

4) To avoid misunderstandings in the administration of the church, all problems related to the work should be considered in consultation with our national brethren.

Each of these propositions met with opposition, but all of them passed with a slight majority. Then each motion was assigned to a committee which would study the best way to put it into operation.

To Edward, Lila, and a few others, it seemed that the future now held more hope of progress. Louis, on the other hand, was far from convinced that the Mission was on the right track. But he decided to go along with his wife's hopeful attitude and seek the Lord's guidance as he tried to face the problems which he knew would soon come up . . . if any of the proposals should actually be put into practice.

Chapter Three

Suffering with Christ

Several years have passed since that memorable day when Edward made his revolutionary propositions, and for some unknown reason, no real changes have been seen in the work. But Lila has not given up. In a slow but persistent way she has influenced the younger missionaries in favor of a reconstruction of the Mission's basic attitudes, and one day, after she had been assigned to the planning committee, the subject of "our relationship with the national church and its self-determination and independence" has come up again. It is Lila's opportunity.

"I propose that we invite the pastors," she said that afternoon, "to a meeting in which they can tell us how they feel about our relationship with them, what is right and what is wrong with the way we do things. We need to know firsthand what they think about us."

The suggestion was accepted and circular letters soon went out to each national pastor and lay leader, indicating that a meeting was to be held where everything they felt was wrong with the relationships between missionaries and nationals should be stated — in the most kindly, positive way possible, but with all frankness. The missionaries were also advised of the meeting by a note in English.

When the invitation reached Leonardo, he felt a heady mixture of emotions. He supposed he might be dreaming, but if so, he felt quite sufficiently awake to start writing down a long list of the things that had bothered him for years and that he had never told Louis. Then, still holding the note in his hands, he began to think about what results this might produce. Would he really be able to say all that he felt? In the final analysis, would it be prudent to open his heart to these foreigners who were so strong in their own opinions? A deep sigh escaped him as he thought of the possible consequences of such an encounter.

Then he remembered that his friend Manuel was staying at the Bible Institute at the time, with other pastors who had come into the city for their quarterly retreat. Leonardo decided to go and talk the matter over with him. As he entered the main building of the Institute where he had received so much blessing during his school days, he always felt a certain pride and satisfaction. In spite of all the problems involved, what a joy to be a servant of God!

He strode into Manuel's room without knocking and wasted no time on preliminaries. "Have you seen this letter? Do you think it can really be true? Do you suppose they really want us to tell them everything we feel, or is it just pure politics? If we tell them everything, will we fall from their good graces and get thrown out of our churches the way Samuel did? Remember, he said very little that time at the Convention, but from then on he was pushed aside more and more, and the missionaries influenced the churches so that no one wanted him for pastor and he finally had to quit. But the fact is that he was thrown out."

Manuel listened gravely and Leonardo kept on talking. "It looks to me as though this may be a trap. I have six children, and even though I'm not old yet, I've given the best years of my life to the ministry and . . . well, with a situation like the one Samuel faced, I don't know what I would do! We don't have any Social Security or pension or anything like that to count on. Frankly, I don't know what to do. I feel as though I ought to talk to don Louis before I make up my list, don't you think?"

For a moment Manuel thought the matter over and then replied, "I think this whole business is unjust. We can't talk about the bad things these people do because, after all, they've done us so much good! Regardless of their mistakes, I for one feel a deep debt of gratitude to all of them — because they have brought us the light of the Gospel. I'd say the responsibility of criticizing is theirs, not ours, in spite of all our gripes against them."

Leonardo considered that point as Manuel continued, "However, I think it might be healthy for both groups to express everything they feel and why they feel that way."

"Man, you're right!" Leonardo was excited. "That's a better idea! Why don't we go to see don Louis and suggest that he and dona Lila ask the other missionaries to consider that idea? It would be much less embarrassing for the pastors, and . . . well, if I'm going to say something critical about the missionaries, I think they ought to be able to tell me what they have against me, too. Let's go!"

"All right, let's go," Manuel agreed. "I think he's in the office right now."

"Oh, but probably dona Lila isn't there," Leonardo recalled suddenly, "and it would be better if she were."

"Yes, she is — I saw her arrive in the car a few minutes ago. She's probably been out visiting, because don Louis brought the motorcycle today. Come on." Without further ceremony they started for the office.

When Louis saw them approaching, he said to Lila, who had come in to consult him about a prayer letter, "Here come Manuel and Leonardo — I hope they aren't going to ask for another advance. They always end up the month with no money. I never saw such dreadful administrators. But I already told them that unless I receive a counter order from higher up, I'm not going to loan them any more money, because they ought to learn to live with what they have."

"But, darling," protested Lila, "what would you do if you had six children and only twenty-five or forty dollars a month for food, light, clothing, and everything else? It isn't that they're bad administrators, they just don't have enough! Sometimes I wonder. . . ." At that instant the two pastors knocked, and Lila could not go on.

Both Manuel and Leonardo, feeling a bit cautious and unsure of themselves, indicated that they would like to have a word with Louis right away. "Well, if you like," the missionary told them, "perhaps we can make an appointment for tomorrow. I have a great deal to do today and I also have my class in personal evangelism within two hours and I need to study. I've given this course for the past four years and I pride myself on studying for every single class so that the material will be fresh in my mind. So, if you don't mind, tomorrow. . . ."

"Very well!" exclaimed Manuel in a strangely excited voice, "but that is exactly the sort of situation we want to discuss. You have sent us this invitation and we want to be sure what it means!"

Influenced by a meaningful look from his wife, Louis reluctantly agreed to talk for a few minutes with his inopportune visitors, although he felt considerably irritated by their insistence. "Go ahead," he told them as courteously as possible. "I'm all ears."

Manuel took the initiative. "Don Louis, we don't know what has prompted this invitation from the missionaries, but whatever it may be, Leonardo and I feel that it would be unjust for us to tell you what we do not like about you, unless you agree to do the same with us. Nearly all the pastors have many things to suggest, but . . . even though we are more than grateful especially to you, don Louis, it would seem that more positive results would come from a hearing of both sides rather than of just one."

Louis was frankly surprised at their suggestion. He promised to pray about the idea and pass it on to the people who were responsible for the meeting, while Manuel and Leonardo left his office rejoicing that he had listened to them.

Before many days had passed, the rumor spread around that a meeting was to be held in which each group was going to say what it thought of the other. Finally the leaders of the Mission accepted the idea officially, convinced that the Holy Spirit was guiding. As one of them said, this seemed the best way to go, "especially in these days when we feel that we are no longer one, but two."

In addition, all the missionaries were asked to pray much about the meeting and be ready to accept the reproach of Christ, if that should be the Lord's will.

Chapter Four

Hour of Confession

The great day of revelation finally arrived. As special speaker the committee had chosen Dr. Narchants, a man of much missionary experience and spiritual power who had been born in South America, of European parents, and ever since childhood had absorbed the influence of both cultures with no loss to either. A devotional message by Dr. Narchants initiated the day's program right after breakfast.

That first morning, undoubtedly guided by the Holy Spirit, he began: "I would like to base my meditation on this occasion upon chapter one and verse fourteen of the Gospel of John." As he read, Lila was conscious of a sudden tug at her heartstrings, and she turned sideways to glance at Louis as though to say, "There's my special verse again."

When he had read the Scripture passage, Dr. Narchants bowed his head. "Our Father," he prayed with a voice full of emotion, "Thou who art worthy of all honor and glory, this morning we ask Thee to open our blind eyes, to penetrate our deaf ears, and to arouse our indifferent hearts. Speak to us, Lord, speak to us! Help us to respond to Thee. Humble us, until we are able to see our mistaken attitudes of pride and self-sufficiency so that we may carry out Thy work. Lift us up so high that we may see Thy glory. Teach us, until Thou canst say of each one, 'Well done, thou good and faithful servant.' In Christ's name, Amen."

Just this simple prayer seemed to move many hearts, even the disinterested ones who had come to the meeting expecting to write letters, knit, read, or even get out a mailing while lending half an ear to the messages and discussions.

As Dr. Narchants got into his message, he seemed full of conviction and power from on high. "Brethren," he said earnestly, "I am convinced that the Holy Spirit has given us this text not only to teach us the precious doctrine of Christ's incarnation, but also to show us His complete lack of prejudice and His integration into a society which was infinitely different from His own. The proposition 'The Word was made flesh and dwelt among us' has several logical implications.

"First. Regardless of how strange and different we may find the culture where we serve as missionaries, if we come as ambassadors of the King, we must be able to surpass all human expectations in regard to our identification with those we serve.

"Second. If you will forgive my theology here, I'd like to suggest that Christ was aware of the fact that His very divinity made it impossible for Him to communicate with us as human beings, and so He descended and became man — in order to reach us with a language that we could understand.

"Third. Christ humbled Himself knowing full well all the indignities and cruel injustice that He would have to suffer. He made His decision with a complete picture of what it would cost Him to die. Yet because He loved us so much, He consciously and deliberately made the decision to humble Himself unto the death of the cross, so that you and I might have the opportunity of communion and friendship with Him."

The development of these three points made a profound impact on each listener and even before the speaker finished, there was conviction of sin in many hearts. The message closed with these words:

"Many times our cultural and emotional circumstances lead us down to the very depths of despair, and reveal how impossible it is for us to overcome them, from the human point of view. But if Christ Himself could leave His throne, His heavenly comforts, His glory, and His truly celestial culture in order to win us, then surely by faith we too can overcome obstacles of any kind in our service for Him, until we come to experience the joy of saying with the Apostle Paul, 'I have finished the course, I have kept the faith. . . I am become all things to all men, that by all means I might save some.' "

After the message there were a few moments of prayer; no one doubted that the Holy Spirit had spoken. It seemed that the time of prayer and spontaneous testimony could have continued indefinitely, but there was a schedule to be followed, and so the leader of the meeting stood up to direct the singing of a final hymn.

After a ten-minute break for coffee, a bell rang to call the pastors and missionaries back to the chapel. As they entered, their faces seemed to reveal a feeling of expectation and suppressed excitement — the next hour was scheduled as the beginning of the frank, personal observation, which had been announced as the main business of the morning.

The singing of "A Green Hill Far Away" was first. Prayer was offered. Then Edward, who fortunately or unfortunately was to preside at the meeting, began by saying:

"I don't know much about the medical profession, but I understand that when a person has cancer, it can often be cured by removing the cancerous cells. I believe that in recent years our relationships here can be compared in some ways to a chronic and malignant cancer, and this morning, on this operating table, with the Lord as our Surgeon, with love, with sincerity, but with all frankness, we are going to try to get at the cause of our cancer and remove it. May each one ask that the Holy Spirit control him, so that he will neither offend nor feel offended at what we may say or . . ." speaking to the national brethren, "what you may say to us. I have decided that we should follow a suggestion made by Manuel and Leonardo — that is, that each person should simply mention one thing, without comment on either side, while the rest of us listen, and if it should be necessary for us to do so, let us ask the Holy Spirit to give the victory before we leave this place.

"Now then, if no one objects, I am going to sit down. When someone feels that he wants to say something, just stand up, say it, and we will make a note of it here. Before we begin, let us sing the first stanza of 'My Jesus, I Love Thee.' Here are the words:

My Jesus, I love Thee,
I know Thou art mine;
For Thee all the follies
Of sin I resign;
My gracious Redeemer,
My Saviour art Thou;
If ever I loved Thee,
My Jesus, 'tis now!

After the hymn there was a long silence, and yet the atmosphere seemed charged with the Spirit of God.

Finally it was Leonardo who stood up and said hesitantly, "I believe that this occasion is very significant for the progress of the church. I'm sure that all of us have been waiting, perhaps with some trepidation, for this day. I have many things to say, but I believe I speak for all the churches when I say that the gratitude which we feel for our missionary brethren is far greater than our resentment. How could we ever repay all the good which you have done for us by bringing the light of the Gospel to our hearts? Our gratitude is not only personal, but national. I want to be sure that this expression of appreciation is noted quite literally by the secretary before I begin the list of the small things which separate us so painfully.

"What I am going to mention is nothing of importance, but

. . . it upsets me greatly that when you missionaries visit my home, you do not eat what I offer you. I am poor, but what I offer is with love. I shall never forget the day when my wife gave a glass of one of our favorite refreshments to one of those present here this afternoon, and after he had tasted a little of it, he threw the rest out the window. We saw him do it. He thought we didn't, but we did. And we felt very badly about it."

Another silence.

"What I can't stand is that every time we make an appointment with a pastor, almost invariably he comes late," said Louis. "I must confess that this bothers me so much that I have very nearly come to lose all respect for you."

"As a national," said a pastor from one of the city churches, "not necessarily as a Christian, but as a loyal citizen of my country, it bothers me that the missionaries claim this as their second fatherland and yet never learn the National Anthem."

Amadeo, one of the best educated of the pastors, spoke next. "Well, since we are speaking so frankly, I am going to confess that what bothers me is the imperative, condescending, superior way in which many of our missionary brethren ask for things. It would seem that they have learned nothing of courtesy, or else they don't consider us worthy to be treated as friends and companions. And now that I am on my feet, I am going to add something more. I feel a strong resentment against the brother seated here to my right because I found out that he charged the Mission for the dinner that he served my wife and me one time when we were in his home. Rosita, the girl who works in the office, is my witness. It made me feel as though the invitation were nothing but a farce, not a matter of love and friendship, but simply a political move. Nevertheless, I am glad to say that this very morning the Lord has touched my heart and I . . . I forgive you."

He sat down with a smile and an outstretched hand for the startled man next to him. A tall, gray-haired missionary with years of administrative experience spoke next. "I'll have to admit that several things have concerned me. Since the very beginning, when I was put in charge of supervising the work, I asked the pastors and national workers to present me with a weekly report as to the number of houses visited, sermons prepared, tracts distributed, and so on, and I know for a fact that many of you have put down work which you did not do. There are many things that bother me, but nothing — *nothing,* I repeat — bothers me so much as lying. I beg of you, my brothers in Christ, if you want to help us, please avoid this type of thing." He sat down and put his head in his hands.

Ignacio, a veteran graduate of the Bible Institute, stood up. "Well, I . . . maybe I shouldn't say this," he stumbled. "Please forgive me if I am wrong. What bothers me is that some of you . . . well, almost the majority of the missionaries seem to spend more time going to the market, putting children in bed, talking among themselves, and running to the post office than serving directly in the work. And another thing I can't stand is that every time I invite a missionary to eat with me, or I am invited to eat with him, his wife always has to be consulted first. I wish you could be like us, putting your wives in the proper place where they belong, according to the Bible."

Trying to keep his voice calm, a second-term missionary spoke up now. "None of the things which my colleagues have mentioned bother me," he said, "but I am tremendously affected by the fact that every time you ask to borrow money from me, you almost never pay it back, or if you do, it is long after the time you promised. The point isn't so much that I need the money as that it seems to be a lack of moral integrity. As a missionary I don't feel that I need to beg your forgiveness but rather implore all of you to be what you ought to be in the light of God's Word, responsible for every action as new creatures in Christ."

A short, stocky national pastor was next. "When I meet a missionary on the street, either on foot or in a car, he is always in such a hurry that he has no time to greet me. Missionaries never have time to exchange a word of casual, friendly conversation, at least not with the natives. At first it affected me more than now, but I still notice it."

Another pastor added, "What really distresses me is that when people are present who do not speak English, the missionaries speak English anyhow, and often we even hear our own names mentioned. Since we can't understand what is being said, we feel that you are saying something against us. It seems quite discourteous and thoughtless — at least it makes us feel highly uncomfortable. And another thing I don't understand is why missionaries need to take such long vacations in the United States. How can anyone possibly be vacationing all that time? I sometimes wonder if it isn't rather an escape from all the frustrations caused by working with such impossible people as we are. . . ." His tone was sarcastic, but his facial expression revealed a nervous uncertainty as to whether he might have said too much.

"Perhaps it is because I come from a different culture, as some have suggested," said an attractive, young lady missionary, blushing with embarrassment at what she was about to say, "but frankly I am distressed by the fact that so many pastors don't seem to care about their appearance. Sometimes it is obvious that they need a bath, or they don't use deodorant, or they haven't shaved, or they should have on a fresh shirt, or they need a haircut, and . . . and many other things that I probably shouldn't mention." Her voice grew strong with conviction. "We must remember that people judge the Gospel by what they see in us!"

Now it was a layman, a lawyer who held a leading position in one of the local churches, who spoke up. "Many things have bothered me," he stated firmly, "but two in particular. One is that the missionaries apparently do little more than take photographs and write letters. Among ourselves we sometimes joke about this parody of Mark 16:15 — 'Go ye into all the world, take pictures, and write letters to every creature.' And then the missionaries take a whole year's vacation! Forgive me if this sounds exaggerated, and of course I know it is, but as the saying goes, usually 'where there's smoke there's fire.'

"The other thing is that . . . well, this happened fourteen years ago, but it still bothers me and I'm not sure that it won't happen again, so since we are speaking from heart to heart, I'll mention it. When Miss Noody fell in love with Fernando, the Mission made her resign and leave the country. I've been told that Mission regulations state that missionaries are prohibited from marrying nationals. Frankly, it seems to me that this is a law which goes very much against the spirit of the Lord. We feel that it is an offense against our country, and even a sin, because God has made all men equal. God's only prohibition about marriage is that we should not be unequally yoked together with unbelievers, with non-Christians. Furthermore, why should we inhibit these missionaries to such an extent? If one of them falls in love, and is counseled about the potential problems of such a marriage and still persists in wanting to marry some lowly member of our worthless society, why . . . instead of making things hard for him, we should help him. I don't see anything wrong with loving the people with whom you work to the point of deciding not to leave them anymore!" Rodolfo sat down with an apologetic smile, knowing that he had mentioned a sensitive subject which was generally taboo in public conversation.

No one else said anything for several minutes. Then . . . "I'll have to confess," admitted an older missionary whose work was directly concerned with the churches, "that what worries me is the fact that I never can count on the pastors carrying out the agreements we make at the annual meetings. More than half the resolutions made there are completely forgotten . . . never carried out at all. I don't know whether this is because the pastors are so disorganized, or because they get up late, or what. I think that as servants of the Lord we should budget our time. This isn't a matter of culture, but of administering the precious time which God has given us to use for Him. More than once I've been bothered by the fact that I arrived at your homes at eight o'clock in the morning and found you still in bed."

Antonio, pastor of a small church some miles away from the capital, was next. "The thing that offended me most was the time when dona Anita died, and all of us went to stay up with her all night, according to our usual custom. We wanted to show our love and sympathy, but . . . to our amazement her husband told us to go home because it was getting late and everyone was going to bed! We felt terrible about that. Then when we arrived for the funeral, we found that the body was put into a car and driven off to the cemetery so fast that it seemed like a soul carried off by the devil, as we say here. I understand that it is a matter of custom and culture, but in our country it is customary to take the dead to the cemetery in a very slow procession, and I think the missionaries should follow the same custom. 'When in Rome, do as the Romans do.' "

When Antonio sat down, a man got up who had served as a leader among the evangelicals of the country for many years. "Something happened several years ago," said Petronilo, "which has bothered me terribly ever since, and I don't think I'll ever forget it. I'm sure that many of those present will also remember it. I'm referring to the time when we were organizing the big assembly of pastors. You named me as the national representative and Mr. Lynn was the Mission representative. I was very happy to have the opportunity to serve. But it turned out that all the power or responsibility I was supposed to have was nothing but a farce, as so often happens when we deal with missionaries. We nationals really have no authority at all.

"For example, Mr. Lynn offered a sum of money which he said we should administer as wisely as we could. We were delighted to have someone put confidence in us, even though we realized that we weren't the world's best administrators. But things did not work out as he had said. He not only failed to keep his word, but he put another missionary in charge who had to approve everything we did. Then he made us change all our plans, without any reason. And when we went to print the program, the whole thing had to be done over again because the photo of a local man was ahead of someone else's. I was burned up."

Several of those present looked at one another with a nod that said plainly, "Yes, we well remember that affair!" Petronilo went on talking with such fire in his eyes that everyone could see that, with or without reason, he had suffered a great deception:

"That wasn't all. The next morning, I was tactfully made to understand that the special speaker who was coming should have nothing less than the Presidential Suite of the hotel! I didn't say much about it at the time, but I'm telling it now and you can judge for yourselves. These extremes of pride and vain-glory leave much to be desired. Well, I do want to forgive all this, and yet I also want to recommend that when such conferences are planned for other occasions, these same mistakes not be made. The man who is representing the Mission should have real authority, stick to his word, and put some trust in the nationals working with him. Of course, I sometimes got the idea that Mr. Lynn himself wasn't to blame for all the changes that were made, nor was it his fault that the speaker demanded such ridiculous prestige and honor.

"If the Mission wants the work to progress, then give us the tools, teach us how to use them, but don't keep laying down new conditions and changing the rules. Tell us within what boundaries we should move, make our limits clear-cut, and then let us work in our own way. A man loses all desire to work when he is treated as a child."

When Petronilo sat down, a veteran missionary named Frank Britton rose to his feet. "I don't want to appear as though I know everything," he began, "and I am afraid I am guilty of many of the things which have been mentioned this morning, at least from the viewpoint of my national brethren, but . . . I believe the person who suggested we speak from both sides was guided by God. In a sense it gives us an emotional balance, and I thank the Lord that these principles are being followed in this meeting. Now unfortunately I have several items to mention, with humility before the Lord but with strong convictions.

"First. Throughout my years of experience here, I have observed that the greater part of the national pastors have no interest whatsoever in progressing intellectually, in spite of the opportunities we give them. This brings very bad results in the Lord's work. It's one reason we are losing so many of our young people, who are better educated than their pastors.

"Second. I don't know why, but you pastors are too timid about talking to your leaders about the Gospel. Every time you encounter someone who is a little bit important, ranging from a top national leader all the way down to a mere small-town politician, you come running to the missionaries to help you approach him — if you do anything at all. This makes the Gospel look like something foreign or imported.

"Third. Maybe I shouldn't mention this, but . . . well, I'm going to say it anyway. Many of you pastors don't use your heads and you allow your families to get far too large. You can never support or educate so many children adequately. I think a pastor should use his intelligence about this matter.

"Another thing that has given me gray hairs is the way you spend so much time talking about nothing. I mean — it's all right to talk to one another, but if you would only talk about something worthwhile!

"Well, this is the last point, and I'll sit down. It seems to me that all of you tend to be communist sympathizers, and as a result you have developed very little appreciation for us and for our country. I think politics should be something completely separate from the church, although as Christians we should stimulate the growth of civilization in every way, but we must open our eyes to the dangers of Marxism, which is sometimes introduced covertly in our very midst because of the sympathy which you offer it.

"Forgive me, but now that I am on my feet I have thought of one more thing. So please excuse me if I am talking too long. Something that has bothered me tremendously is the fact that you nationals never do anything well. You begin an endless number of things but you never finish any of them. That's the reason many of us don't like to give you responsibility, because we can't count on your fulfilling it. You may not show up, you may change you mind, and so forth. Sometimes when we *do* depend on you, you leave us completely defrauded because you don't really do the things you promise; or if you do, it's at the last minute and poorly done."

The six things which Frank had mentioned seemed to fairly explode in the air. All were related to intimate problems of family, integrity, and fatherland. Edward was tempted to stand up and announce a hymn, give a ten-minute break, or something equally drastic, but as he prayed for guidance the Lord led him to start singing quietly, there in his seat, "Search me, oh Lord, and know my heart today. . . ." The others joined in, until the soft chorus seemed to fill the room with peace and victory.

When the song was ended, Ruth Anderson, known to all as Miss Ruth, stood up sobbing, unable to utter a word for a few moments. Immediately all eyes were turned in her direction. After she was able to control her emotions enough to speak, she said in a quavering voice:

"When God called me to this place, I promised Him that I would be faithful until the very last days of my life, regardless of what might happen to me. As you know, all my springtime years have passed now, and I have left them here. But one thing has never ceased to trouble my heart. I don't believe I am mistaken because I know you all too well. I saw many of you come into the world, and others I saw born into the family of Christ, but . . . what has bothered me all these years is . . . is. . . ." She struggled to stop the flow of tears with the help of a crumpled, lacy handkerchief, and finally summoned her courage to go on: "It's that you have never been frank and honest with us . . . you are traitors, deceivers, pretentious, ungrateful! To our faces you say one thing with a lovely smile and behind our backs you say just the opposite and hurt us. You aren't sincere. But I forgive you all and I hope you will forgive me."

When Miss Ruth finished, the room seemed to vibrate with all kinds of feelings. Dilia, a national worker who had spent ten years serving with the association of churches, whispered to Miguel, "God is speaking to us. We shouldn't close this meeting until we have reached into the farthest corners of our hearts to clean out all the filth which is hidden there." As she spoke, she thought, "I for one don't have anything to say. Or if I do, it isn't anything vital to the progress of the work. They are things that probably no one has noticed and would be better unsaid."

But in that moment the phrase from Song of Solomon, "the little foxes that spoil the grapes," passed through her mind, and she knew that she should speak. She stood up.

"I've been struggling with myself," she confessed, "and I am thankful that I can declare before the Lord that I feel no resentments toward anyone. God has given me the victory over many of the things which have been mentioned, and they no longer bother me. I believe I have learned how to practice what the Bible teaches about love. Nevertheless, I am going to mention a few items of secondary importance — perhaps to some of you they may seem very essential, but the Lord knows that for myself I am telling the truth. I believe that as human beings we are free to act according to our own conscience and that what is bad for one may not be bad for another. But as Christians, and especially as Christian workers, we have another standard of conduct to which we are obligated to measure up. Now the things I'm going to mention — some I have seen, others I have heard about, others I have experienced, but all are *true*. Here they are:

"First. The missionaries forgive but they never forget. They always remember the offense we have done to them, or the slip we made years ago. I am sure of this because of the way many of you have expressed yourselves to me about others.

"Second. The missionaries always suspect the nationals of some kind of moral weakness or unfaithfulness, and never have the faith to believe that Jesus Christ, who began the good work in us, can really perform it.

"Third. The children of the missionaries talk disrespectfully about the nationals and often offend them. Perhaps this gives us an idea of what is said about us in their homes, I don't know. I do know that I have experienced this sort of thing myself.

"Fourth. The missionaries don't judge the relative value of things and spend too much time in activities that for many of us . . . I repeat, not for me personally . . . are objectionable. I think this has to do mostly with the few individuals who go on trips every week, or who spend hours talking on the radio, or who never lose an opportunity to play with model airplanes, or who spend so many whole days boating on the lake.

"Fifth. The missionaries seldom or never take part in the social life of the people. Their parties are always in their own language. They claim they feel no race prejudice or that sort of thing, and yet — their unguarded actions belie their words.

"Sixth. In spite of the tremendous amount of love they profess for us, their children are not sent either to the public school, or even to the evangelical school, so that they can learn our culture. I suppose this isn't important, but I pass it along without any personal resentment whatsoever."

When Dilia finished speaking, everyone seemed to be breathing a bit easier. It was obvious that some did not agree with her in the least, while others were nodding their heads in a strong affirmative. It seemed that the silence was not going to be broken, until all of a sudden, in the back row of the attractively decorated, six-sided room, Roger Rogers got to his feet. Since the earliest years of his ministry, he had been characterized by a decided frankness, which sometimes produced negative results; but nevertheless all the pastors had learned to listen carefully and even reverently to his pronouncements because of the hard truth they so often enveloped.

"I don't know how long this meeting is going to continue," he began, stroking his chin in a characteristic gesture, "but I don't want to miss the opportunity of saying something." At that, everyone turned around to be sure of seeing him, since he was not very tall. "Several things bother me, too, and I am going to mention them right now. For example, when I give the pastors money for their expenses, they never give me detailed reports. They just write down bus fares, meals, etc., in a general way. I think they should understand that I am responsible to give account to others and I need complete details. I must confess that many times I have suspected that you really spend the money for other things and then put it down as expenses of the work.

"The other point is that the pastors have no concept of what the Lord's House should be. The Bible says that God has taken us out of darkness into the light. This means we should be making some progress every day. Well, frankly, I feel very troubled at the way you decorate the churches — even with crepe paper of every imaginable color! And not only for Christmas, either, although more than once I have become ill just to see the way you put a picture of Santa Claus, perish the thought, on the wall next to a Scripture text. I would like to see an attractive church, but — well, beginning with the colors you use to paint the benches, the buildings look more like restaurants than churches. The benches at the Playa church are blue, those at Cerrillos are red, and those at Palmares are green, just to give some examples." He threw up his hands in a mock gesture of horror and sat down, leaving his audience smiling not only at his remarks but at the way he still mixed up his words and phrases in their language. One of the favorite stories going the rounds for years now was of the time he had been preaching at Barillas, during his first term of missionary service, and had finished the sermon by saying in all innocence, "If anyone would like to accept salvation tonight, please raise your foot."

With a glance at his watch, Edward stood up. "Our time has gone, and I have the impression that almost all of you have said what you wanted to say. But just in case . . . does anyone else want to mention something?"

No one spoke, but Manuel raised his hand to indicate that he had something on his heart. Edward said, "Let's sing a stanza of a hymn while Manuel comes forward. Or would you rather stay where you are, Manuel?"

"It's all the same to me. I haven't too much to say, but if you wish, I'll come to the front."

"Yes, please," urged Edward, for reasons he could not quite explain.

The hymn he chose was:

I gave My life for thee,
My precious blood I shed,
That thou might'st ransomed be,
And quickened from the dead;
I gave, I gave My life for thee,
What hast thou given for Me?

As they came to the last line, Manuel started forward and then stopped to ask Edward how much time he should take. "Whatever you feel led to use," was Edward's reply.

"Brethren," began the tall, neatly dressed pastor, his dark hair and eyes contrasting sharply with his white and gold smile, "In the first place I would like to praise God for the precious opportunity that He has given us this morning. I believe that if we had done this long ago we might have avoided some of the fantastic mis-impressions we seem to acquire along the way.

"Now I want to mention two things that I don't believe anyone else has referred to. As a pastor I have experienced a bit of a problem with myself and with my church regarding the matter of offerings. Ever since don Louis informed us that the churches should all support themselves, he began to teach us about tithing and stewardship. I well remember the fine classes he gave several years ago. I learned almost everything, but this morning I want to confess that I have put very little of it into practice. I now recognize that the excuse I had is not justifiable, because each of us must give account to God for his own actions, not those of others, but I still think it will be helpful if I mention this to you.

"When our missionary brethren began to talk so much about tithing and tried to get the pastors and churches to do it, I was one of the first. . . . I know now that I was wrong, but . . . well, I asked myself if this doctrine was applicable only to us, or to missionaries as well. And with this malicious attitude I went around asking different pastors if they were using the missionaries as their examples regarding tithing. Unfortunately it looked as though none of you do tithe, even though you receive much more than we do. At least that's the way it seemed up to last year, and, brethren, I must confess that this has taken away my own willingness to tithe and also my authority to teach others to do it.

"Someone has said that no one can give what he doesn't have, and if you don't teach us with your actions, it follows that we won't teach the church members either. The same thing happens with church work in general. As a church, if you will pardon the comparison, we are like a fifteen-year-old girl who thinks she knows everything, but when she is face to face with the realities of life, she makes a lot of mistakes.

"It has bothered me greatly that you ask sacrifice of us and yet you yourselves are not willing to sacrifice. You ask us to tithe and you do not tithe. You ask us to have a passion for lost souls and you have lost your own passion. You ask love and you do not practice it. You ask spiritual integrity and faithfulness and you do not have it yourselves.

"Forgive me for mentioning this so openly, but we seem to be in some sort of confessional, just among ourselves, and I believe all of us are brethren in Christ and prone to commit errors. But I feel I should mention the following incident just to reinforce what I have been saying. Leonardo told me some time ago that one day when he and don Louis were evangelizing one of the better residential areas near the church, they came to the home of the owner of the textile factory, and when they began to speak about the Gospel, don Jacinto was surprised to learn that don Louis was an evangelical, even though they both belong to the same Country Club. True or not, don Louis?"

Louis nodded and then bowed his head in shame before the Lord. In his relationships at the Club he had followed the policy of soft pressure in his witness for the Gospel — too soft, perhaps.

"The other day," Manuel continued, "I went to the barber shop near the Bible Institute and began to evangelize the barber while he was cutting my hair. As we were talking, he said, 'Everything you say is very nice, and I imagine it may even be true, although you have some gringos that should never call themselves evangelicals. I had two customers . . . well, yes I *had* two,' the barber said, 'because I couldn't stand one of them and one day I gave him such a poor haircut that I figured he'd never come back. He acted so superior and ordered me around in such a way that I hated to see him come in.' Well, the barber kept on clipping the back of my head and finally told me about the other gringo, who by the way is don Glen, who, he said, was a wonderful fellow and really lived what he preached.

"Now as you can see," said Manuel, "we need to realize what an influence we have as leaders of the work. It's true that the national church is supposed to be moving toward independence, even though we seem to be doing it at a snail's pace, but the fact remains that spiritually and socially we still look to the missionaries for guidance and inspiration, and whatever you people do or don't do is immediately reflected in the national church. I think all of us should ask forgiveness of the Lord and of one another. We aren't here to play around. We are responsible for the salvation of this entire country!"

Manuel turned humbly to Edward. "I'd like to suggest that each one of you seek out the brother or sister in Christ with whom there may be any wall of separation, and right now, this very morning, let's straighten out our relationships. Let's go all the way. Then, as we finish, let's form a big circle, join hands, and then kneel in prayer as an act of consecration before God."

Head bowed, Manuel left the platform. Immediately Edward was on his feet, and with his voice full of emotion said, "I would like to ask forgiveness of Joaquin. I have offended him." Turning toward Joaquin, one of the pastors from the capital, he spoke softly: "Do you forgive me, Joaquin? You know what I am talking about. If you do, come and let us embrace one another."

Joaquin, profoundly moved, started toward the platform. Edward stepped down, and there, beside the piano, they embraced so enthusiastically that they scarcely noticed a vase of red gladiolas, which was knocked to the floor. It was obvious to everyone, looking at their smiling faces, that a real transaction had just taken place. Then the two knelt side by side.

Louis was next. He went to Leonardo to ask forgiveness, and after him came so many others that it became necessary to move the benches in order to make the circle which Manuel had suggested.

When everyone was kneeling, a radiant-faced Lila suggested, "Let's sing the hymn, 'I Surrender All.' " They sang as never before, each word seeming to take on a new and deeper meaning. It was as though they were glimpsing heaven. They breathed together and even felt their hearts beat together as they entoned the words of the chorus:

I surrender all!
I surrender all!
All I have I bring to Jesus,
I surrender all!

As the hymn ended, Edward whispered, "Dr. Narchants, would you please close with prayer?" Immediately these words were heard:

"We thank Thee, Lord, for the power of the Holy Spirit. We thank Thee because Thou dost not reward us according to our iniquities. We thank Thee for this precious experience which has made us see the light of a new era in our work, which is truly Thy work. In Christ's holy name, Amen."

Everyone stood and Edward dismissed them: "Don't forget that this afternoon we will meet again at three o'clock. I believe we have diagnosed our illness and perhaps found something of the remedy. Now we must plan a balanced diet in order to keep ourselves healthy in the future. You are dismissed."

Chapter Five

Confronting Reality

That morning seemed destined to go down in history. But in spite of the sweet spirit which had prevailed in the chapel, not everyone was happy. Out in the kitchen Marie Adams was quite perturbed because the service had gone so long that lunch had gotten cold several times over. Knowing the mood she was likely to be in, Edward hurried to find her and beg her pardon for having let the meeting run so much longer than planned.

"You sometimes act just like these natives around here — you're never on time," Marie snapped. "You men don't seem to have any consideration for those of us who have to feed you. Don't you realize that while you're enjoying yourselves we're suffering? We're almost two hours behind schedule!"

With an understanding twinkle in his eye, Edward begged, "Forgive me, Marie — in the future I'll keep the kitchen crew in mind. I promise."

Surprisingly enough, Edward soon found that Marie wasn't the only person who was less than happy. In spite of all the tears and pardons and newly exchanged ideas, a persistent root of bitterness lay deep in many hearts. Louis, for instance, had felt very much moved, and yet he could not overlook the fact that practically none of the nationals had shown any gratitude. "Just what I wrote to Jim," he thought, "these people will never appreciate us. Better just go back to the States and let them go on their merry way and see how they get out of their difficulties." He couldn't help recalling a Spanish proverb that he had learned as a tenderfoot missionary many years before: "Take care of a crow and he'll pluck your eyes out."

For Gilbert Jones, one of the newer missionaries, the whole thing was fantastic, incredible. Sitting in the dining room staring out the window, he scarcely knew when grace was said. "How is it *possible*," he asked himself, "that these people dare to say that we don't work, that we don't tithe, we don't sacrifice? I can't believe it! This is terrible! We've got to change these wrong ideas about us." His heart seemed to race with frustration. "Why, how many times have I practically taken the very shirt off my back to give to one of them! There's scarcely one thing they ask of me that I don't give them gladly!" Wryly, he remembered Charles Tuttle, who had dressed exactly like the men in the rural area where he worked, and who had spoken their language so perfectly that he scarcely had any accent at all, and yet even he had been harshly criticized. So was identification really the answer?

An even stronger reaction was felt by the professors of the Bible Institute. Amadeo, Juan, Joaquin, Manuel — many of these men had been practically illiterate when they'd first arrived at the Institute! "Why, if it hadn't been for our own personal financial sacrifice and our spiritual interest in them, they would never have gotten any education at all, much less reached university level," thought Sam Evans. "But that's life. That's the way they pay us back for all we've done for them. Exactly what I've always expected."

Some more, some less, but the more they thought about the meeting, the more impractical it seemed to have been. That was certainly the feeling of fourth-term missionary Alfred Jay, who had not been moved in any direction except that of reaffirming his own personal convictions about these nationals, who would never get anywhere with their negative way of acting and thinking.

Nevertheless, for Lila the meeting had been wonderful. She realized that its consequences might be painful in some respects, but she couldn't help rejoicing at all that had already been accomplished. In the dining room she happened to sit beside Dr. Narchants, and he too had obviously been very much impressed with all that had happened that morning. Turning a bit in her chair, accidentally bumping Louis on her other side as she did so, Lila began interrogating Dr. Narchants.

"Tell me," she smiled eagerly, "what do you think may be the final results of the meeting this morning? Do you think it was worthwhile? Could you give us any ideas about what we ought to do now? Are we on the wrong track?"

Vivacious Lila was so excited that her words tumbled out in a heap and Dr. Narchants winked at Louis while he tried to sort out her questions in logical order. But his answer was serious.

"I think everything that has happened has probably been good. I am sure God has guided, and yet . . . I wonder if there shouldn't be more provision made for the future. All the bad things, or at least a good share of them, have been brought out into the open by both groups, but there has been almost nothing of a positive nature. I think every circumstance and situation has a good side as well as a bad, and if we don't have enough self-discipline to be able to see both sides, we might easily get off on the wrong track, as you suggested."

"What do you recommend?" As she listened, Lila scrutinized the kindly face rimmed in steel gray hair and concluded that Dr. Narchants' appearance of strength with sweetness must be the result of his long years of personal contact with his Lord.

"Well, I haven't thought of anything in particular, but . . . in general terms, what all of you need is to learn how to communicate with each other. From what I heard this morning, it would appear that you missionaries have no idea what the people here think or feel, nor how you could influence them to be of greater help in the work. And yet on the other hand, from what was said about vacations and that sort of thing, I gather that the national brethren are practically one hundred percent ignorant of the way the missionaries live and operate. If this is really the case, I would suggest that one of these days you get together to talk about the reasons for each situation."

"What do you mean?" Lila pressed. "Would you mind being a bit more specific?"

"Well, just that as soon as possible I think you should explain to the pastors just why you receive more money than they do, why you have to write letters and take pictures and travel to your home country and educate your children elsewhere, and so forth. It seems to me that such an explanation is indispensable if you hope to arrive at some concrete understanding with the national church. Otherwise this same spirit will continue, and many of your pastors will blindly — and ridiculously — believe that the missionary never works and merely exploits the circumstances and happenings of the church. This sort of misunderstanding and misinterpretation is undoubtedly at the root of all the so-called anti-missionary spirit."

Lila agreed thoroughly. Thanking him for his advice, she pushed her chair back from the table and stood up to look for Edward. She finally found him deep in conversation with Miss Ruth, who was apparently offering a few suggestions. Lila coughed slightly to get Edward's attention, indicating that she wanted to talk with him. He responded by letting her understand that he would be glad to listen to her after Miss Ruth had finished.

Lila could not help overhearing as Miss Ruth took her leave of the younger missionary: "Follow my advice and you'll be glad you did. I haven't lived here all these years for nothing. The changes can't come too drastically, because they will hurt, but I do believe they have to come, one at a time, and more often."

Meanwhile Manuel, Joaquin and Leonardo had seated themselves at the other end of the table and noticed that Lila was trying to talk with Edward. "Look, there's dona Lila," remarked Leonardo. "That little lady always has good ideas. I wish all the missionaries could be like her. Of course, the best thing would be for her to have married a man like Eduardo, but . . . such is life."

Joaquin laughed. "I thoroughly agree with the person who said that marriage is like throwing dice. Once the die is cast, there's nothing to do but accept the results."

"Ah yes, but wouldn't it be better to *win* all the games of life?"

"Look," broke in Manuel a bit impatiently, "what did you think about the meeting? Don't you think we are progressing somewhat? What do you say — should we leave things as they are, or press for some solutions right away?"

Just then Rodolfo approached their end of the table. "May I join you? From what I can gather, you are discussing something interesting."

"Sure, come and sit down," Manuel urged him. "We're just talking about the results of the meeting this morning. What's your considered opinion as a lawyer?"

"Well, I haven't thought about it at any great length, but just offhand I'd say that since we've started we might as well go all the way."

"What do you mean by that?" Joaquin looked startled.

"All right, so now we've taken the clothes out to air, let's give them a good shaking! For instance, maybe this is the psychological moment to request that the Larsons are not sent down here again and that the Larkinses do come back.

Remember them? They were really the kind we need. They really knew the Lord — none of this new trend of casting doubt on the Scriptures and trying to substitute the social graces for Christianity the way some missionaries do. And don Jorge was always ready to help with anything we needed. With him we never had to make an appointment for every little thing and then get told we had ten minutes and no more."

"Yes, but it isn't as easy as it looks," said Leonardo. "When the Larkinses were about to leave, they had an idea that the other missionaries weren't in favor of their procedures and they told me they might not be sent back. We asked the Mission about them and they said they were going to assign them to work at the Home Office. By the way, do you know what that is?"

"I can imagine," drawled Rodolfo, "but to be quite sincere, even though I was converted when I was nine years old, grew up in the church, and practically lived in the shadow of the missionaries, I have never fully understood how the Mission operates. One thing I do know is that when they began talking about making us independent, they mentioned a certain group which controls all the titles to the property here. I think they have their office in New York."

"Don't tell me it's on Wall Street!" laughed Manuel.

"Could be," Rodolfo replied. "Everything is possible. Listen, what if we should ask the Mission to explain to us a bit more about its operation and procedures? Maybe it would help us understand its problems better than we do now."

Joaquin shook his head. "That won't ever happen. The only hope would be for a few of our old-style missionaries to pass on, but — some of them are pretty young yet."

The bell rang, signaling the time to return to the next meeting which, according to the printed program, was designated for discussing the problem of getting more candidates for the ministry.

As the group began to gather in the chapel, some of the missionaries had the feeling that there was no use staying in the country any longer. All the things that had been said in the morning were just one more proof of the way communism and anti-missionary spirit were infiltrating the country, in their view. What hope did the future hold for them and for the work in general, the way things were going?

Edward opened the meeting with prayer and then smiled apologetically. "While we were in the dining room, dona Lila came to give me a suggestion which I personally think is a very good one, but it would affect the program we have outlined for this afternoon. Nevertheless I promised her I would discuss the matter with all of you, to see what you prefer to do. I wouldn't want to have us lose the pace of the sessions but neither would I want to close my mind to the possibility of a change."

At that moment Amadeo raised his hand and demanded somewhat rudely, "Tell us please what she suggested, so we will have some basis for deciding whether the program should be changed or not. Otherwise we will just be losing time."

"Well, if you insist, I'll be glad to mention what dona Lila suggested. She had a talk with Dr. Narchants during lunch, and . . . well, I think it would be better if she herself told you. Would you please come forward, Lila?"

From the back of the room Lila tried to get across the idea that Edward, not herself, was the one to speak, but the pastors insisted and she finally rose to her feet. "All right, in a few words I'm going to say that I'm convinced positively that God spoke to us this morning. I believe everything which was said was valuable, but . . . it was hard for all of us. While my husband and I were eating lunch with Dr. Narchants we talked a bit about the morning sessions, and he said he had gotten the idea that even though we work together, we seem to live in two different worlds. I got the impression that all of us, both pastors and missionaries, painted a pretty ugly picture this morning. Here we have a group of men and women who are called sons of God, ambassadors of the King of kings and Lord of lords, and yet no one works, no one tithes, no one loves, no one understands! If that is really the impression of one side or the other, rightly or wrongly, we ought to stop right now and find the reasons why this is so, and then find some solutions. I propose, if at all possible, that we explain some of these things here and now."

Lila sat down without looking at anyone. She was courageous and intelligent, but speaking out in public about such a highly-charged subject was not easy for her. Her heart beat rapidly and her cheeks were fiery red. Probably the pastors were criticizing her right now as another example of a missionary who did not know her proper place! Their words had been razor sharp that morning about American wives who bossed their husbands.

Now it was Rodolfo who signaled for permission to speak, seconding Lila's proposal that a better relationship should be sought immediately through a frank discussion of the problems which had come to light. Edward asked for a standing vote and the motion was carried unanimously. "Well, someone has to start," Edward observed with a dry smile, "and even though we have no law about it, I would like to suggest that we try to follow the model which the Lord gave us in the morning. Remember? We were speaking out in a more or less alternating order. I think that for the good of all of us, both groups should explain insofar as possible why they do what they do. Now if someone is ready to begin, the floor is yours."

Roger and a few other missionaries of the old school were seated in the front row, fairly bursting to speak.

"In the first place!" exclaimed Donald, rising to his feet, "I would like to explain to the brethren here that we certainly do tithe. I am sure that every single missionary here present gives a tithe or more. What happens is that there are so many needs throughout the country that we have to divide up our help in different ways. I believe that in good conscience before the Lord I can say to you this afternoon that there has never been an occasion when I have seen a need that I haven't tried to help. Please don't misunderstand me. The Bible teaches that your left hand shouldn't know what your right hand does, and that is doubtless the reason you don't see our names on many of the offering lists, but believe me, we all give at least a tenth of all that we receive. What happens, I suppose, is exactly the same thing as when we give you a Christmas gift or any other kind of a gift — you never say thanks. With our tithes many of you have studied in the Bible Institute, others of you have sent your children to school, others have had your doctor bills paid, and so forth. Furthermore . . . ."

He was interrupted by Rodolfo. "Could I have permission to make an explanation, don Donald?"

With a pleasant spirit, Donald remained standing while Rodolfo spoke. "It seems to me that even though some of the pastors are embarrassed to admit it, we have to 'render to Caesar the things that are Caesar's and to God the things that are God's.' I know for a fact that many believers and pastors have received the personal help to which don Donald has referred. But precisely there is the mistake. If we are thinking about a national church, we should give ourselves to it, and be subject to its institutions. From now on, I believe, every missionary ought to give his offering *through* the church of his preference, giving it through the church so that this may be a lesson for all of us in addition to a demonstration of love for the Lord."

Turning to Donald, who was a little upset by now, he smiled and begged, "Forgive me, don Donald, but these explanations are necessary, don't you think?"

Donald stood silently for a quick second, thinking to himself, "If we aren't careful, these nationals are likely to put us in discipline!" But turning away quickly from his prejudice, he said aloud, "Well, as I was saying, although I may have forgotten some of what I was going to say — since Rodolfo's interruption rather surprised me — it seems to me that this matter of the offering is something in which you shouldn't interfere. These are personal things between me and my

Lord. I don't know if my other colleagues share my point of view, but that is the way I feel."

Rodolfo immediately asked for the floor, and suspecting that Edward might not give it to him, called out, "Don Edward, question of privilege!" Edward nodded and Rodolfo continued along the same line as before, only this time a bit more concretely.

"I don't know whether or not I can make a motion," he began, "but if it is time for that now, I suggest that the missionaries join our churches as regular members. In this way, it seems to me, they can influence the way their money is used and distributed. I am taking for granted that from now on, all of the missionaries will consider the church as their strategic base for influence and action."

At that point, Donald, imitating the trick used by Rodolfo, called out, "Mr. Chairman, question of privilege!" Everyone laughed heartily, then grew serious again. "I believe the national church ought to support itself and shouldn't expect any more help from the Mission or from the missionaries. It has already received a great deal and yet its progress isn't worth mentioning."

The nationals felt a strong, swift reaction against his use of "a great deal!" Almost unconsciously, a debate between Donald and Rodolfo was in full swing, with everyone listening intently. Rodolfo was the last to speak, declaring, "The church, as you seem to think, ought to support itself — but if you missionaries don't want to take the reins and be in charge, then I think you should pass into the category of ordinary believers, and that means you should be in the position of giving offerings to the church just like everyone else. It always helps to have a Christian brother who serves as an inspiration along that line!" His last sentence was noticeably sarcastic.

Practically everyone was upset by now over this lengthy argument, and besides, there were other things to be discussed. Edward took over and said that both sides were right and that in the future it would be better to avoid making personal references in anything that might be said.

Louis decided it was time for him to speak up. Firmly but cautiously, he made reference to the information which had been requested about the *modus operandi* of the Mission. "I must confess I didn't realize you folks would be interested in knowing how the Mission operates," he began, "and as director of this area I feel responsible for not having explained it long ago. It seems to me that this is a subject which involves a number of points, so I'll try to be brief — but I don't want to sit down until I have made it clear.

"In the first place, a Mission depends to a large extent on the interest and prayers of the churches who support its work. In our U.S. headquarters we have people who take care of sending out bulletins and letters based on information which we supply constantly from here, although many of us also write personal letters directly to our friends as well. The Christians in the homeland want to know what we are doing, and what their money is accomplishing, and so we keep them informed by means of what we call prayer letters. We are obligated to do this quite often, although certainly not as incessantly as you seem to believe, so that our friends up north will remember to pray for us and send their economic help for the missionary program."

Joaquin interrupted to ask a question, and as he did so, a feeling seemed to sweep over the room that the afternoon was going to be one long interruption. Asked Joaquin: "Why do you receive so much more money than we do?"

"Well," replied Louis, "because when we are accepted as missionaries we are told that we must seek commitments for a certain amount of basic support before we are allowed to come to the field. I think that right now I am going to turn the floor over to Manuel, because last year he went with us for our year of furlough — or vacation, as you call it — and I want him to explain how we raise money and interest supporters to help with our building projects, technical equipment, and other needs of the church here. Manuel, would you be so kind?"

At that moment Manuel was caught completely off guard, since he was busy thinking of a long list of suggestions that he planned to give as a climax to the afternoon's meeting, or so he thought. Finally, taking a deep breath, he grinned, "I don't know where to begin, because if you want me to be very frank, my trip to the United States was a bore. When don Louis asked me about going with him, I was thrilled, but once I got there, I had a headache for three straight months because I didn't understand anything of what they were saying. Is that what you wanted me to say, don Louis?"

Louis smiled. "Well, not exactly, but I think you're going in the right direction. Go on."

Manuel turned his head to look at Edward. "Well, as I was saying, I not only felt like a complete fool, but the situation was made even worse by all the food they make you eat up there. I got filled up to here. . . ." The wry expression on his face, coupled with a gesture indicating that it had been just too much, made everyone suffer along with him. ". . . the food was nothing but salad, gelatine and that mixture of sweet and salty foods that they always serve on the same plate. But I must confess that the experience was a real blessing to me because I think it helped me understand how Americans feel when they come here as missionaries. Not being able to speak is horrible — you feel like a child. And I think they probably get just as bored with our food as I did with theirs. One day don Louis invited me to a Latin-American restaurant and I'll tell you, the rice and beans and fried plantain tasted wonderful!" Everyone burst out laughing.

"Well, that isn't what I intended to say. Forgive me, but the truth is that there is so much to tell. What I can't forget, and I think this really does answer don Louis's question, is that I thought you just went up there and practically swept the money off the streets and picked it off the trees, but it isn't that way at all. I'll never forget one day when we had to drive 500 miles to a certain missionary conference, and not only did they neglect to give one cent of money to don Louis, but they told him he had only five minutes to speak because that night they had so many missionaries scheduled to tell about their work! We went through many experiences that bothered me terribly, although I never said much to don Louis. One thing was that several times they expected don Louis and me to sleep in the very same bed, and other times I had to sleep with men that I didn't even know — imagine!"

The look on his face made everyone laugh all the harder at his last remark, until some were even crying. The meeting was almost ruined because the laughter went on and on as though it would never stop. Finally in the midst of all the hilarity, Manuel continued, "I hardly understood any English, but don Louis told me several times that he asked the people and the churches to pray for me and the ministry that I represent. The truth is that you have to write many letters, travel all over, be separated from your family, speak almost every day, and almost never know the results. One thing that impressed me is that cars there are like dogs here — they're very cheap. Don Louis told me that a man has to go to school for a minimum of sixteen years before being accepted as a missionary, and then he can't go to the field until he has what the Mission stipulates for his salary. Well, forgive my long speech, but I think this answers the question."

Edward took over now. "It's interesting to recall that fifty years ago our grandparents in the United States were more or less passing through the same transition as you are here, although in a different way. There were no cars, nor good wages, but even so, each church developed strong members — morally, socially, and spiritually — until there was a strong laity in the church. As a matter of fact, all the members of our Board of Missions in the homeland are laymen except one."

At that instant, as though popped up by a spring, Manuel jumped up and exclaimed, "Pardon me, but I would like to illustrate what you just mentioned! When don Louis and I arrived up north, I went to hear my first sermon in English. I didn't understand a thing, but the man who spoke did it with real passion and fervor. When he finished I asked don Louis if he were the pastor of the church, and don Louis knocked me cold when he said the man was a layman. It's a fact that we ought to make the development of more lay leaders one of our goals. Perhaps we ourselves won't receive the benefit, but those who come after us certainly will."

Everyone nodded in agreement and it looked as though at last the meeting might be producing some positive results. Edward, looking at his watch, prayed silently that God would keep control of the time which remained, knowing full well that this day was going to be unforgettable in the annals of the Mission and of the church.

Chapter Six

Revolution in the Making

Edward took over again to say that the time was going fast and that the remaining minutes should be used to give specific suggestions, whether practical or not, with an open heart and mind.

Amadeo was the first to get up, asking, "Should we make motions or only suggestions?"

"I would say you should give every concrete suggestion that you can," replied Edward.

"Well, then," continued Amadeo, "I'd like to suggest that you write to the Board of the Mission to ask them to open the door and send us three specific kinds of missionaries. I think we are wrong in thinking that the words Mission and missionary imply that you have to work only with the institutions and churches that are now in existence. I believe these words imply much more. Here in our country we have six million people and five million of them don't know Christ. Yet we seem to spend more time trying to get along with each other than trying to preach the Gospel! Well, specifically I'd like to recommend that they send us:

"First. Pioneer missionaries. What I mean to say with this is that they be people who are willing to evangelize new areas, and there to help and teach the believers to organize autonomous churches as soon as possible. It seems that nowadays the missionaries all arrive with the idea of training national leaders, and I suppose that is why they don't do personal evangelism with zeal the way Miss Ruth still does it even today.

"Second. Missionaries who are willing to become integrated — at least sixty percent integrated — with the people of our country, both in the work of the church and in giving help of a social nature, are what we need. They should become ordinary members of the Sunday schools, and work just like any other layman works in the church after finishing his regular day's work. I mean they can do some kind of institutional job for the Mission during the daytime. Furthermore, for this type of workers, I think the term 'missionary' should be avoided; just call them brethren. In other words, we would consider them as a part of the congregation, helping in the visitation, serving on committees to plan Christian Education, music, and so forth for the church. Then if they fail us, the effect won't be so drastic. My idea is that instead of referring to them as missionaries, we should simply refer to Brother So-and-So.

"Third. Specialized missionaries. These can be put in charge of innumerable jobs. For instance, depending on what profession or training they might have, they could open an evangelical industrial school where our believers could be taught a definite trade. This would raise our living scale and as a result it would affect the entire economic level of the church. I don't know if you understand me, but what I mean is that we should establish some kind of special program which will elevate the position of our members in some way or other.

"This could include, if you wish, brethren who come from the United States with some experience in agriculture, to teach our believers how to better cultivate their land. It could include men who understand political science, who could teach us ideals for our political parties: They wouldn't have to get mixed up in our internal affairs, but they could teach us a great deal. All the believers up to now who have gotten into politics have been lost from the church, either because they didn't have enough spiritual maturity to resist the temptations they met there, or because the church abandons them and then tries to ask their help later on when they have some authority in the government. Many times we complain and say they don't help us, but it's our own fault. We must let them know that it is possible to be a good Christian and a good politician at the same time.

"The missionaries in this category could also include men who are specialized in human relations and social work, men who can teach us the value of public relations, and so forth. The time of the missionary is not over. There is still room, and there will always be room until the day when as a church we shall have fulfilled our task of establishing at least one congregation in every town of 5,000 or more people. Until we have a church in every town, neither nationals nor missionaries should talk about not needing help from the Mission. Once we have these congregations, trained and well-developed, self-supporting and self-sustaining, integrated into our national church program, then we can say we no longer need the Mission. That would really be something for our country."

As Amadeo sat down, it appeared that his words were churning up many minds which had not thought before that, after all, today there is not so much need for specialization on the part of missionaries as for multiplicity in the types of ministry to be carried out. Rodolfo, who always liked to select words for such situations, said to himself, "What we really need is to divide the work into penetration, direct evangelism, and consolidation of what we already have — which is why we need the three types of missionaries that Amadeo has mentioned." He was strongly tempted to stand up and ask to speak, but after the discussion with Donald he did not have the nerve.

Joaquin, who had been vacillating for a few moments, spoke now. "I'm going to stand up so you can see me, speak clearly so you can understand me, and sit down quickly so you will appreciate me." The old joke provoked a short bit of laughter. "It seems to me that Amadeo has put his finger on the sore point, although frankly — I'm not in favor of eliminating the word 'missionary.' I believe that this morning someone mentioned that don Marcelino, the barber, doesn't want to see or hear of anyone with the name of missionary, but . . . there are missionaries and *missionaries.* Someone has said that there is a little bit of everything in the Lord's work. Furthermore, you must realize that in many of our fields, the connotation of the word 'missionary' is of great inspiration. Just listen to the words of this hymn composed by a very simple believer, which you'll hear sung all over the rural areas:

My prayer to my Saviour
Is that He permit me to serve Him,
For in my soul I feel a joy
Like that of a missionary.

Blessed Christ, do not deny me,
I long to serve Thee as a worker,
Give me love, give me passion,
Like that of a missionary.

"As you can see, I hold the position that the term 'missionary' should not be eliminated, but rather amplified and used more widely to include our national evangelists, workers, and so forth, so that the concept of missionary work may become integrated into all our thinking. After all, if tomorrow or the next day we are to be a strong, aggressive church, we should also be a missionary church, shouldn't we? Well, this isn't really what I intended to say, but I couldn't resist the temptation.

"What I really want to express is that I know for a fact that many of our missionary brethren from the United States are horrified when we present special music by our own national trios, choirs, and soloists. I realize that they probably do sing like parrots, but they are all we have! Now it seems to me, if Amadeo agrees, that to his list of specialized missionaries we should add those who know music and come, not so much to perform it, as to teach others. For example, Mr. Charles sings beautifully but has not bothered to teach me and a few others who might be interested in developing our small talent along that line.

"Of course the ideal thing would be to start a school of sacred music, sort of a traveling school, perhaps — planned so that believers of different levels of talent could progress up the scale of music study. We Latin Americans have music in our very bones, and if anyone winds us up, we just can't stop. The creation of a Latin American ministry of music is badly needed in our day. If a church wants to dry up, all it needs to do is take music out of its services. But the churches that want to advance should use not only lots of music but quality music as well.

"In addition, those of you who know music should stimulate our national composers. They don't know much about harmony, rhythm, or tempo, but with your help they could create their own appropriate hymnology which would be capable of reaching the deepest sentiments of our believers.

"Oh — one more thing. The same ought to be done with some of us who aspire to be writers. Help us to publish what we write, even though you may not agree with us! If you don't, you may never be able to develop national writers and theologians of quality."

As Joaquin spoke, Edward, who knew something about music, reluctantly came to the conclusion that even though he honestly did not care for many of the national hymns and choruses, nevertheless they were actually the ones which gave the greatest inspiration to people in church services. Now he said publicly, "Thank you, Joaquin, many thanks. You have opened my eyes toward a ministry that consciously or unconsciously I had not wanted to share. God bless you."

He paused. "I believe many of our problems originate from the fact that we as a Mission talk over many ideas — many methods and programs — but we never ask our brethren here about what their methods and programs would be. Perhaps in spite of all their ignorance about organization, and their laziness, and their informality about time. . . ." His smile indicated that his words were not spoken in all seriousness, as he went on, ". . . they might be able to produce something more appropriate for themselves and their culture than we can with all our modern advancements. Well, at any rate, this is all turning out to fit like a glove. Thank you, brethren, for your suggestions. Does anyone else wish to speak?"

Leonardo, who had not contributed anything for some time, stood up. "I also feel inspired — and I'm going to mention something that I've talked about privately to various missionaries for years, but none of them has paid any attention. Actually I'm not sure how to express my thoughts, nor what technical language to use, but two things concern me.

"The first is that we have not awakened to the fact that the society in which we live includes certain elements that we could easily exploit for the good of the Gospel. As far as I know, we evangelicals have nothing to compare with the impact of the first communion on children of our society. Not theologically, of course, but emotionally and spiritually and socially our children need something to substitute for the first communion as a highlight of their childhood experience. I believe that if we could give them this type of experience, based on biblical principles and methods, we would gain much territory — because we would not only strengthen our own Christian children, but also attract many other children who go to no church whatsoever and whose parents are no longer interested in their traditional faith. I don't know exactly what could be done along this line, but it certainly ought to be carefully worked out, edifying spiritually, and based on the Word of God, leaving a profound emotional experience in the child."

His words burst like a bomb on Roger, who thought to himself, "Well, here's the seed of modernism already," but he said nothing aloud.

Leonardo went on, "The other thing I wish to mention is that we are not making any definite effort to recruit young men and women for the ministry. The ones who are in the work today are the direct result of personal discoveries made by the pastors and missionaries, but we have no long-range program along this line. Manuel told me that up in the States they have special services at regular intervals, maybe once a year or oftener, but anyhow they are called missionary conferences in which different brethren explain the needs of the country where they serve and challenge the young people to give their lives to the Lord. Don't you think we ought to do the same thing, beginning with the Sunday school? Doubtless it would be on a lesser scale, but God can call young men and women to work in the many areas of need here in our own country.

"I certainly hope that something is done as soon as possible. Can you imagine what we are going to do if we have to wait until our human wisdom ferrets out the talents? Let's allow God to work . . . but let's be the instruments for presenting the opportunity to our young people. Maybe we could begin with a missionary Sunday every six months, or every two months, or every year — but let's begin with something of long range."

Leonardo's ideas somehow awakened inspiration in Elias, who had been quiet during the entire day, and he began speaking in a soft but firm voice: "I am one of the oldest pastors here. I feel as though I am the most useless of all, but now that we are talking about a little of everything, I want to make a suggestion related to elevating the cultural level of the ministry. In the first place, every pastor should be forced to progress. I don't recall whether it was don Roger, or who, but in the morning someone referred to the fact that we pastors do not seem to worry about our appearance or about our intellectual progress. Perhaps true — but both things have their roots in our lack of economic resources. How am I supposed to change clothes every day if I don't even have enough money to provide food for my family? You know what we receive, and you know that it isn't enough to feed ourselves decently. My six children and I eat nothing but rice and beans every day, with a little meat every third day, because my pocketbook just won't stretch any further.

"And I would love with all my heart to study and progress intellectually, but I have neither the means nor the stimulus to do it. Now, for example, if the Mission — as part of the diversification of its ministries — were to help the pastors who want to study, we could do a lot. A pastor who studies can motivate his people better because he understands the implications of what he is doing. Many times I have wanted to throw myself into some big project, but I've been afraid that my ignorance would hold me back from making a success of it — and so I have done nothing.

"In summary, what I want to suggest is that the Mission help us pay for our studies — by correspondence, or however it might be, and that the church raise our income, even if only by a little bit, every time we finish some predetermined course of studies. I have nothing with which to pay for further education, not even to buy books, but if the Mission used the money which formerly went for subsidies on our salaries to help raise the cultural level of the pastors, it would be wonderful. You can put me down as the first applicant!" The request of the "old man," as he was generally called by his colleagues, was made with a smile.

"Together with that, I believe that the Executive ought to buy books for the pastors that would be obligatory for us to read, and that every year we ought to write summaries of these books. All this would help us to progress. Many times I feel embarrassed because the young people in my church know more than I do — and yet I am their pastor! We ought to do something, not just thinking of the future, but right here and now. As the old saying goes, there's no point in undressing one saint to dress up another one. While we're waiting for the day when you start your missionary conferences and all the rest, let's be elevating the level of those of us who are already in the battle but who couldn't get an education for lack of opportunity. While we're waiting for the day when everything will be changed, let's do something with the present. Let's begin right now!"

As Elias gave his final challenge he was in a cold sweat. In spite of all his years in the pastorate, he had never before spoken to such a large group of leaders, and much less before a group of missionaries with their immeasurably higher level of education.

By now, Rodolfo was practically biting his tongue, but he tried to keep from talking too much. The brethren generally enjoyed hearing him, and since he was a lawyer by profession, his words carried considerable weight, to the point of completely changing the direction of many discussions. Finally he could restrain himself no longer and asked permission to speak.

With his face very serene, and a clear mind, Rodolfo began. "I don't know what results this may have, but I sincerely ask the Lord that my words this afternoon will find an echo in your hearts. I positively believe that one of the reasons why we do not advance more systematically in the conquest of our fields is that apparently, as far as I can see, the Mission has no long-range plans. I have the impression that every year we begin some new emphasis. Possibly this is due to the wave of re-orientation that the missionaries receive on their trips back to the States, or perhaps it is caused by the fact that the top leaders of the Mission are ignorant of real conditions here." He paused to study the effect of his words on the assembled leaders. "At any rate, the lack of such plans has resulted in the paradox that some of our institutions, still supposedly evangelical, have ended up in the hands of men with no testimony whatsoever, *because there was no definite plan laid down in the early years.* I know of one Mission hospital which is no longer a means of breaking down prejudice against the Gospel — today it has no Christian influence at all. With the exception of one nurse and one doctor, all the personnel are non-Christian and actually work against our evangelical beliefs. This is a shameful situation! That's why it is so necessary and important to lay careful long-range plans. I am going to take the liberty of making the following suggestions:

"First, that we attempt to conquer education, the press, the radio, public life, and above all, the women. In our culture the woman is the most important figure as far as religious practice is concerned, and for that reason, every young man who marries a girl of a different faith is very hard to get back into the evangelical church. Only if the woman should be converted, but . . . that seldom happens.

"On the other hand, when a non-Christian man marries one of our girls, if she has been properly taught and indoctrinated, it generally isn't too long before her husband begins to sympathize with the Gospel, then to agree with it, and eventually to be converted.

"It's true that our educational systems today are well advanced, in the secular sense, but just imagine what it would be like if all our children were trained and taught in the faith. Ideally, we would hope that every one of them would be converted to Christ — but if not, at the very least we would produce men and women who would be liberal in their thinking and open to be won later with less difficulty.

"On the other hand, I think the Mission could do a lot of good if it would utilize its energies and intelligence by providing scholarship help for teacher training — from high school on up — for all young boys and girls in our churches who wish to become teachers and cannot afford to pay for their own education. In just a few generations, perhaps two or three, we would tip the scales in our favor!

"Along the same line, I would like to add another thought. Those young people who receive benefits such as I am suggesting should agree both morally and legally that they will pay back this help by giving financial aid to some other young person who wants to study for the teaching profession. I suppose this sounds too far-fetched for some of you, but remember — we are in the twentieth century. And as the saying goes, 'the shrimp that goes to sleep gets carried away by the current.' You are witnesses of the way many of our Christian young people have 'failed' examinations just because of their faith. Even though we supposedly have religious tolerance in our country, it is obligatory for every child to take classes in the state religion. And many times, even though the Constitution backs us up and the Ministry of Education authorizes that our children may be excused by a letter from the parents, they still suffer in many ways and are segregated from other activities.

"Unfortunately, our country has fallen into this trap of the state religion — in spite of the example that so many other lands have given of true liberty. Education here will never be completely secular and free until we evangelicals become a respectable minority in the eyes of the Ministry of Education.

"You have all seen the things which have been happening here recently, haven't you? The Constitution guarantees freedom of speech, but oh — how hard it is to get our news published in the papers! Even when we offer to pay! Remember when Dr. Graham was here and we tried to publicize his visit every way we could? Yet in the newspapers of this city not a word was said about him, even though he is a world figure.

"The editor of our morning paper, even though he appears as an international leader in the fight to protect minority groups, was even more cowardly than the rest when it came to publishing a correct explanation of our evangelical position regarding a recent issue. This is a disgrace for our country, but even more so for us — because we have not opened our eyes to the power and importance of the press.

"Let's train our young people in journalism! Let's train them — for example, as photographers. Many of you missionaries, with all the experience you have in photography, could compete with any of the men we have in our national press here, it seems to me, and I'm not joking. Let's open a school where we can teach good journalism in all its aspects, and let's develop a press in our country that will be worthy of the name.

"The papers here have a tremendous influence on the people, not only by giving out information but by interpreting and coloring the news. To teach journalism, I don't believe it is essential for us to bring in a hundred percent evangelical faculty because this is not an institutional testimony. We could use anyone with the necessary ability and training who was not opposed to the Gospel, plus a basic nucleus of Christian men.

"Nor would the school have to use an evangelical name. But it should definitely have a large number of evangelical students. Our voice would then be heard in public opinion, not the way it is now when we suffer so many injustices and can't even publish them. If we could, people would be shocked — many evangelical schools closed, believers killed, churches locked up or burned — eloquent testimony that we are the victims of a well-planned, long-range type of persecution, yet practically no one is aware of it.

"Furthermore, this new legal approach of saying that only technicians and professionals can enter the country as missionaries is also a very potent type of persecution. That new Law 400 may very well be our downfall. According to that, foreigners can enter our country and practically monopolize our industry, exploit our workers, and even — if you will pardon the expression — prostitute our women, whereas if the foreigner should be a missionary he has to be a specialist, and in some cases deposit an exorbitant amount of money for his visa. This is what I call persecution in depth!

"Oh, my brethren — we need to conquer the press, the economy, and political life. With this last thought I am going to finish. Please be patient with me — you know the old saying that if you give a Latin American your hand he'll take your foot. Since you are listening to me now, I'm going to take advantage of my opportunity.

"Anyhow, for several years now I've been told that we evangelicals shouldn't take part in politics. I realize that this aspect of public life is often corrupt, but politics itself is not what's bad. Rather, the problem is that those who run political activities don't have any conscience about the true needs of the people. I know that when we talk about these things, people say we're leftists or communists and little by little we're eliminated from intimate communion with other Christians. But all of us who are Christians ought to serve God, and as citizens we are also morally and socially obligated to contribute to the needs of our country.

"We Christians are the ones who can look impassionately at social injustice, and at the extreme exploitation of our human and material resources by our own national leaders as well as by foreign interests. Oh, how I wish the church would encourage the young men who want to study political science, or would give definite backing to the formation of a political institute where the goals and objectives would be similar to those I suggested for the newspaper institute! We must understand, brethren, that as long as we have men and women dying of hunger and lacking in the most basic necessities of modern society, we are going to be helpless to stop the advance of these communistic doctrines."

As Rodolfo spoke the last words, his inflection seemed to indicate that his lengthy discourse had come to an end, and suddenly a ripple of applause broke out that grew into a great wave of hand-clapping for nearly five minutes.

Finally the enthusiasm began to wane, and Edward stood

up. Although he had applauded warmly, he realized that Rodolfo's ideas were extreme and would produce negative reactions in many of those present. For that reason, cautiously but firmly, he announced:

"Friends, two kinds of emotions and passions are tussling in my heart. One would carry me in the direction of my old convictions and ideas, but the other is forcing me to open my eyes to the truth. I am in favor of what Rodolfo has said *only* when and if we take great care to keep our basic convictions where they belong. That is, not ahead of the facts, nor behind them, but within the framework of the situation as it really is, and within the limitations of the principles of Holy Scripture.

"As Rodolfo spoke, I was thinking to myself: What might be the results if all the mission boards working in Latin America, with all their financial resources and manpower and affiliated church organizations, were to hold a continental conference? Couldn't we then put into practice many of the things which have been suggested here?

"Another thing — Joaquin tells me that he has already obtained permission from the Ministry of Education to begin a special night course to prepare adults for their high school examinations — and he says that many believers are planning to attend, as well as non-Christians. I don't doubt that a lot of people will begin the course, although I'm not sure that very many of them will finish it; but at any rate this is one method of obtaining a good many benefits for the church and for our society."

Edward intended to go on speaking, but a hand went up at the left side of the room and frustrated his idea of going into more detail about his suggestion for a continental missionary conference. What he had in mind was for a large group of leaders to meet and discuss the possible coordination of certain ministries which were common to the various countries and missions, in such a way that better results could be produced.

He thought, for example, of the need for a Christian university . . . an accrediting agency for Bible schools . . . evangelistic publications . . . wider use of television and motion pictures . . . so many possibilities!

More than once he had heard people say that the problem of the United States State Department was similar to the problem of mission boards — that is, *what* is done is not nearly as important as *how* it is done. The *how,* Edward thought to himself, is the key factor. Many church leaders had told him that a crust of bread given in a loving and understanding way was far more effective than a banquet given without affection and in an un-Christian way.

Although his thoughts were racing one after the other as a result of all that had been said during the afternoon, Edward was aware of his immediate responsibility — directing the meeting. And someone was very eager to speak. Nevertheless, for a few seconds he stood thinking, suddenly coming to the conclusion that he agreed with a rather revolutionary idea Rodolfo had given him some time earlier. Perhaps, after all, it would be good for missionaries to take their general education in the homeland and then come here for their theological studies and specialization in Spanish. It's not a bad idea at all, he said to himself, although . . . whatever would we do for teachers, for textbooks, or for appropriate courses? Well, if the idea should be workable, it would not only provide a real-life anthropological and sociological laboratory for future missionaries, but would also greatly help them to understand the culture and learn better ways of communicating with the people. Worth considering!

Chapter Seven

Dawn of a New Day

The raised hand belonged to Agur, a consecrated Christian who seldom spoke in public, but whenever he did it seemed that God gave him something specific and significant to say. His life was so holy that almost nothing more could be wished for. He had been related to the work almost from the beginning, and in spite of the trials and tribulations which the years had brought, he still seemed remarkably young and alert.

When Edward nodded for him to speak, Agur left his seat and came forward to the platform. His action surprised almost everyone, for not only had he come to the meeting without an invitation, but Edward had not said anything to him about going forward. A feeling of extraordinary expectancy began to pervade the room and more than one heart beat faster. What was Agur going to say? His long years of experience in the work inspired much respect for his opinions. His personality was somewhat domineering, and his long white beard worn in a style reminiscent of the last century lent him an even more imposing air.

Walking over to the pulpit, Agur courteously asked Edward

to step aside so that he could open the compartment and take out the large pulpit Bible. He opened it to the thirteenth chapter of John and began to read in a clear, resonant voice beginning at verse one:

"Now before the feast of the passover, when Jesus knew that his hour was come that he should depart out of this world unto the Father, having loved his own which were in the world, he loved them unto the end. And supper being ended, the devil having now put into the heart of Judas Iscariot, Simon's son, to betray him; Jesus knowing that the Father had given all things into his hands, and that he was come from God, and went to God; he riseth from supper, and laid aside his garments; and took a towel, and girded himself. After that he poureth water into a bason, and began to wash the disciples' feet, and to wipe them with the towel wherewith he was girded.

"Then cometh he to Simon Peter: and Peter saith unto him, Lord, dost thou wash my feet? Jesus answered and said unto him, What I do thou knowest not now; but thou shalt know hereafter. Peter saith unto him, Thou shalt never wash my feet. Jesus answered him, If I wash thee not, thou hast no part with me. Simon Peter saith unto him, Lord, not my feet only, but also my hands and my head. Jesus saith to him, He that is washed needeth not save to wash his feet, but is clean every whit: and ye are clean, but not all. For he knew who should betray him; therefore said he, Ye are not all clean.

"So after he had washed their feet, and had taken his garments, and was set down again, he said unto them, Know ye what I have done to you? Ye call me Master and Lord: and ye say well; for so I am. If I then, your Lord and Master, have washed your feet; ye also ought to wash one another's feet. For I have given you an example, that ye should do as I have done to you. Verily, verily, I say unto you, The servant is not greater than his lord; neither he that is sent greater than he that sent him. If ye know these things, happy are ye if ye do them."

Agur closed the Bible and looked up. "I am thankful to God that by pure coincidence I find myself here in this meeting today. I didn't know a thing about it, but as Romans 8:28 tells us, 'all things work together for good to them that love God.' Nevertheless, I have learned many things from you throughout the day, and many of you have given some really good ideas, but . . . none of you has mentioned the most essential thing of all."

When he said that, every person present looked around as if to ask, what on earth have we forgotten to mention today? It seemed as though practically every possible area had been covered, but Agur claimed something else was lacking! After a brief silence, he went on:

"Here in this passage which I just read, we have the concrete, living illustration of what John 1:14 signifies. I don't know whether Dr. Narchants was planning to speak from it this evening or not, but I feel that I should say something about it. Notice, if you will, the verbs, and the tense in which they are used. Jesus was conscious of His divine citizenship in heaven and yet He did not come to be served but to serve. Blessed is the man who decides to follow in the footsteps of the Master, and rejoices in doing the will of that One who bought us with His precious blood. I am now old and perhaps there is not much hope of my taking part again in very much activity, but . . . permit me to suggest that if I were your age, either as a pastor or as a missionary, this is what I would do."

He paused again, as if to make sure that his thoughts were all in order. His hearers, quite certain that Agur had something of significance to offer, settled back for what promised to be a real five-point sermon with all the trimmings.

"In the first place," he stated, "I would seek with all my heart to be filled with the Holy Spirit. Unfortunately, this is something we are often afraid of, but this fear is completely groundless. In Acts 2:39 God has promised the power of His Spirit for all. You seem to try to complicate everything so much nowadays that you have reduced the Holy Spirit to mere methods and different theological forms. But the Holy Spirit is the clear-cut answer for all our problems. All that you have mentioned is very good and very necessary, but if it isn't done by men who are full of faith and the Holy Spirit, you will fall right back into the very same errors. Today you have begged forgiveness, but tomorrow you may offend each other again. Today you are full of convictions and zeal, but tomorrow you may be frustrated and unhappy in your service for the Lord.

"It doesn't matter how the Holy Spirit is manifested. God descends to each heart and each circumstance, to the spiritual and intellectual culture of each individual. Now I realize that when the Holy Spirit has pre-eminence, we still face many problems, but those problems have immediate solutions. I feel that you spend too much time talking — you don't *do* anything. Faith should be constant action.

"In regard to the baptism of the Holy Spirit, or second blessing, or being filled, whatever you prefer to call it, this is something that is received by faith just like salvation. One has to believe by faith that God, through His Son Jesus Christ, gives daily victory over sin, every day, every hour, every second. When faith is professionalized and the devotional life mechanized, one gets to the point where you seem to be. You want to evaluate everything. You want to reason it all out — but you are on the wrong track. The Bible says we are to sow the seed and God will give the increase.

"Another thing I would do if I were in your shoes would be to work as though the rest of you didn't exist at all. I don't know why you are so worried about what you ought to do together if you still haven't finished the task that you ought to do separately. Each and every Christian is responsible to evangelize the whole world. I don't suppose any of us here can cover the entire world, but that is because we are finite, not because we do not have the responsibility to do it. You pastors — don't be so dependent on the missionaries. If you don't do anything with the means that you already have within reach, it's doubtful that you will do anything with more. Let's set our affection on things above, not on things on the earth.

"After all, humanly speaking, the missionaries have no obligation whatsoever to come here and help us, right? If they come, it is because they are responding to God's call, because they have learned that every man who receives the light should pass it on to everyone he can reach. What happens is that all of you are like the dry bones of Ezekiel. You are nothing but bones — lots of ideas, lots of organization, lots of long-range plans, but no life. The bones did not come back to life until the Spirit came from the four winds, and likewise you won't be successful unless you give liberty to the Spirit of God. Let each church worship God in the way it seems best, worshipping Him in spirit and in truth. In the end the results will all be the same, because God's thoughts are higher than our thoughts. Remember that Jesus said 'blessed is he that doeth these things.' "

Agur smiled. As he did so, the eyes of each person in the room were fixed on his face. His saintly expression and white beard made him seem an even more venerable figure.

"Now for my second point. If I were a missionary, strictly from the human point of view, I would train my mind to the hilt with the history and culture of the country where I was serving. I would be tremendously interested in learning of its heroes, its politics, economics, and religion. After all, our national background means a lot to all of us, and even more to the non-Christian. Let's be realistic. An illustration about a hero from United States history holds little appeal to the unbeliever. But a story from his own cultural environment would hit home.

"Furthermore, I would study the national culture — from both the theoretical and practical standpoints — until I could bring myself to feel equally satisfied with a plate of rice and beans as with a piece of apple pie. I know it is very difficult to become wholly integrated, but it is perfectly possible to become more than fifty percent. After all, if you are going to live here all your lives, you should know how to talk in our language and how to enjoy yourself in our company.

"Speaking of the language, do you realize that what you study in books and what you learn to write is *not* generally what we speak in everyday life? There is only one way to learn our conversation — by conversing. And as far as I am concerned, oftentimes I find more point in a simple proverb of our people than in an entire sermon with exquisitely chosen vocabulary. Why? Because the proverb is something that our people have lived and proved and experienced.

"If I were a missionary, I would make a vow of not reading any more English than the absolute minimum needed for study purposes. The rest of my free time would be spent in talking with people. There are so many people who need someone to talk to them!

"Another thing — I would ask God for the victory over my race prejudice, which I think actually exists on both sides, and maybe a little stronger on our side, even when none of us admits it. Whether I were a pastor or a missionary, I would ask God to give me a consuming passion, each day of my life, for the souls that are being lost. Just because you are relatively sanctified and filled by the Holy Spirit does not necessarily imply that you are active on the front lines of the battle for Christ.

"Then, too, if I were a pastor or missionary, I would choose certain young people from the church and make them leaders — leaders with convictions, leaders with training and indoctrination, so that wherever they might go, they would be stalwarts of the faith.

"Now I can see that some of you pastors look very smug and self-satisfied, as though you think I am really giving the missionaries an earful. But never mind — now I'm coming to you. The work of the Lord belongs to all of us, but we can't do it effectively if we are not in full fellowship with our brethren. I don't see how some of you have the nerve to stand up behind your pulpits when you're so totally lacking in faith and conviction about what you are talking about. Others of you seem like parrots that just repeat what you learned in Seminary and aren't capable of examining God's Word for yourselves.

"I think our gravest danger today is that we talk, we plan, we ask all the wise men what we ought to do, but we don't ask God Himself. It reminds me of the early disciples trying to find a replacement for Judas. After they had narrowed the choice down to two, *then* they gave God the option. I hope that before we leave this room today we will have taken some definite steps toward God, toward a greater knowledge of Him, so that He can give us the strength to forget our ideas that missionaries do everything wrong, or that they're proud, segregationists or whatever, After all, when we reason like that, aren't we putting ourselves in exactly the same boat? Let's not treat them as foreigners. Let's treat them as brothers in Christ! If we think they are weaker than we on some point, let's help — not criticize.

"Furthermore — and I'm almost finished with what I have to say — it seems that for fifteen years we've been hearing about this plan of turning over the work to the national church. But we never see it actually happen." Agur struck the pulpit with his fist. "And why not? Because you pastors are so lazy, irresponsible, and lacking in vision! Every time you are offered a job which involves real responsibility, you say no, without even thinking of what God might want you to do. You complain that the Mission doesn't turn over title to the properties, but this is nothing more than selfishness. After all, it isn't so important to have the papers as to have the use of the buildings.

"You pastors complain that the missionaries don't like to eat what you offer, but you forget how many times you do the same thing with them — when you turn up your noses at their salads and other things that Manuel mentioned.

"And as far as turning over the work to the national church is concerned, it seems to me that you missionaries like to talk about it but you have absolutely no patience with us. At the first sign of our stumbling, you immediately pull in the reins again. Remember that in our society it is normal to be unstable. Let's understand each other and grow together. May God help us all to talk less and do more!"

With some difficulty, Agur stepped down from the platform, which seemed a bit too high for him — for a man of his age, it was not easy to go down the two narrow steps. Agur had lived through almost every epoch of evangelical work in the country, and so when anyone tried to contradict his statements, he always had a true story to back them up. For example, he had seen with his own eyes one occasion when a missionary and a pastor had actually come to blows inside a church over a minor matter. Incredible? Agur saw it happen.

For that reason, perhaps, and the power of God which seemed to accompany his words, as Agur returned to his seat more than one person was thinking, "That was tough talk, but everything he said was absolutely true." Rodolfo at least had to admit to himself that more than once he had refused to accept responsibility, not because he was incapable of handling it, but out of pure and simple prejudice against the missionaries.

Edward did not know what to do next. For once he felt at least partially guilty of everything Agur had mentioned. It had cut deep. He remembered many times when, in his desire to get the pastors to go ahead, he had tried to carry out programs which he fully expected would fail because he knew the participants were so irresponsible. But, he thought now, the trouble started with me because I didn't have faith to believe that God could work through them!

"God can do it," he thought to himself. "God can make all things new. But we have never had faith enough to believe that God could keep the pastors from giving in to communism, or from selling the properties, or all the other decisions we have faced. It's true that in the past they've seemed to go out of their way to try to humiliate the missionaries rather than to cooperate and help . . . but, well — God healed the paralytic because of the faith of those who brought him in. God can build up His church in spite of the shortcomings of the pastors; He can build it up on the faith of those of us who more fully understand the church and its ministry, even though we may not know quite how best to carry out its program here in a national way. Our faith, put in action by means of national methods, can give the fruit we pray for."

Edward was so absorbed in his soliloquy that he did not realize Agur was now back in his seat and everyone was waiting for him to say something. When he finally came to, it was with a face flushed red with embarrassment that he stood up to say:

"Forgive me — but Agur has slashed us to pieces. Thank you, brother Agur, for your message. May God bless you and continue to use you in the remaining years of your life."

Agur's head was bowed, eyes closed. He felt sure that God had used him and he was praising Him for the opportunity of speaking to such a group as this.

Edward went on, "Before we leave, I would like to give an illustration. The fact is that I've never seen it so clearly as I do now. In the Teen Olympics of our church back home we have a feature called the three-legged race. I don't know if this means anything to you or not, but I'm not quite sure how to translate the name. The idea is that two people are placed side by side, and the right leg of one is tied to the left leg of the other. Then they run the race, holding on to each other. Neither one can run ahead of or behind his partner, because he might fall or even break a leg."

As he explained the game, several missionaries immediately caught the point that he was trying to make. But the pastors obviously understood nothing at all. Edward could tell by their faces that he might as well be talking about a trip to the moon as far as they were concerned. Suddenly, feeling forced into it by the circumstances, he suggested, "Since we have broken all the rules and traditions and protocol today, and since I was authorized to be the chairman of these meetings — with your permission I am going to ask Manuel, Lila, and Leonardo's wife Juana to come forward."

Now the crowd came to life, expectantly.

"Now then," continued Edward, "does anyone else have a two-inch wide leather belt like the one Julio wears? I hope you have yours on, Julio, and will loan it to me for a moment." Julio gave it to him. By coincidence Manuel had just bought one of the same type, which he handed to Edward with the half-joking challenge, "I'll loan it to you if it isn't to thrash me with!"

"Very well," Edward now asked, "could I persuade you to come forward again, don Agur? Please do." A bit confused, Agur walked up to the front of the room once again, and Edward asked him to perform the delicate task of tying himself and Manuel together with the belt, right leg of one to left leg of the other, then doing the same with Lila and Juana.

When Agur had finished, Edward thanked him for his help, and gently commanded his partner, "All right now, Manuel, put your right arm around me. That's it. Now I'll put my left arm around you. Lila, you and your partner do the same. Have the idea all right? This is what we call the three-legged race. If we want to finish the race and arrive at our destination, Manuel has to walk with me, without letting me go. I have to do the same — whether I like it or not, I have to walk the way Manuel is accustomed to walk. Both of us have to give up our personal desires and adapt ourselves to the other if we want to remain on our feet. United by the Holy Spirit, keeping our own individual personalities — but still proceeding together for the same cause. The work of the Lord, the salvation of souls, and the good of our country all depend on the way in which we run together, synchronized in thought and action."

Apparently still not satisfied with mere theory, Edward signaled to the others, "Let's walk from here to the back of the room, and then back again. Let's begin."

The first step was easy, but by step number six Lila and Juana had fallen down. Everyone started to titter, although some felt dismayed that the two women had been forced into such an embarrassing position. Perhaps Edward had gone a bit too far. But the two couples finally arrived back at the platform. Edward and Manuel had tried to walk faster than the opposing team, but Manuel finally said jovially, "Do you know the old saying, 'Dress me slowly because I'm in a hurry'? Well, that's what we have to do. Let's go slow and we will arrive sooner."

By this time everyone in the room had understood the point of the illustration, and there was a general nodding of heads indicating that this type of cooperation was precisely what should be sought for in the future. After the teams had been united and the belts returned to their respective owners, Edward turned the meeting over to Dr. Narchants to give the closing prayer.

Dr. Narchants went gladly to the platform and placed himself behind the pulpit. While his audience bowed their heads and closed their eyes, he began, "Before we pray, I'd like to say something. I believe that brother Edward's illustration here this afternoon has been an object lesson that few of us will forget as long as we live. But I'd like to emphasize that all our efforts to walk together will never produce any results — unless each one of us uproots from his own heart all his racial prejudice, his lack of confidence in others, and his spiritual irresponsibility. None of us can live and work harmoniously together unless we pray for God to fill us with His love, which passeth all understanding. Then and only then will we be able to love and understand each other in the true sense. Our sickness has symptoms which are basically spiritual — and that's why our medicine must come from above. Only God can help us really practice the love described in First Corinthians thirteen. We must remember that He is the One who increaseth strength to them that have no might . . . through Christ which strengtheneth me I can do all things. Now let us pray."

His prayer was long and impassioned and ended with these words: "Lord, surely, what we have seen today of *the other side of the coin* has placed us in a new orbit of responsibility, of action, and of equality in Thy work. Continue moving in the hearts of each of Thy servants in this great continent, of missionaries and pastors alike, until Latin America is like a beautiful spiritual symphony where all our differences of personalities and movements and backgrounds may be blended into one under Thy divine direction.

"And when we have succeeded in instilling these principles in others, help us to remember to say as Thou didst teach us, 'We are unprofitable servants: we have done that which was our *duty* to do.' We ask all these things in the Name of the One who loved us so much that He was willing to humble Himself completely for us, to prove His love with His very death." He was silent for a brief moment, then almost inaudibly breathed "Amen."

The meeting was over. In spite of Edward's rather shocking climax, or perhaps because of it, there was a general feeling that a great deal had been accomplished for the future of both the church and the Mission.

The buzz of jovial conversation grew louder and louder. Three pastors sought out Rodolfo to suggest that he himself was the one to open an Academy of Political Science, whereas they would help by promoting the idea among their young people. Amadeo rather timidly approached Donald to request that a course on good manners and refinement be included in his educational program.

The Mission's director of education went out dreaming up all kinds of castles in the air. "Why haven't we thought of some of these things before?" he asked himself. "A definite program aimed at winning over the women and influencing the home would be precisely one of the most potent weapons we could have. I know my people — and even though it won't be easy, it can be done. Even our supporters at home will be interested, I think, and if they aren't, we'll just have to sell them on the idea."

Lila was off in the clouds somewhere, full of joy and inspiration, satisfied that she had finally seen the answer to her prayers. From now on, she whispered to herself, we will truly be one in Christ, and that is as it should be — so that the world may believe.

Everyone seemed full of big or little ideas to try out as soon as possible. In spite of the fact that there was an infinite number of problems still to be solved on the official level, things would undoubtedly be different from now on. Every single person present at the fifty-seventh annual meeting now knew that, more than ever, each needed the other.

"We know how best to reach our own people," one pastor summed it up, "but we don't have the necessary tools or training to do it. That is where you can help us."

Unfortunately, Roger was an exception to the prevailing mood. His heart was bitter as he reflected on what a waste of time the afternoon had been. Nothing had been done as planned. Usually the meetings closed with a lovely worship service and recitation of the Lord's prayer, but not today. And this year they hadn't even tried to organize the missionary choir which always proved such a delight in contrast to the type of singing they had to put up with in the churches all year. In fact, he muttered to himself, it was an offense to the choir that the whole afternoon had been spent discussing such queer and erroneous ideas about how to evangelize, instead of listening to some of the great music of the church.

Nevertheless, all the talk had produced at least one significant result in nearly all of the pastors: they had not only decided to tithe their incomes, but also to offer their lives more completely to the Lord for the benefit of their country and the needy souls all around them. As one pastor put it, "Each individual who is born into the family of God is under obligation to leave this world a better place than he found it, and this is our task as servants of God, without looking at what others do or don't do."

Edward and his wife were beginning to talk about the possibility of sending a letter to all the pastors, telling them that whenever they heard of a believer who attempted to write hymns — even though the person knew nothing of music — they should send him to visit them so they could help arrange the music and write it down. In time, such a plan ought to help produce a hymnology that would be truly national.

Several of the Mission leaders, talking among themselves, came to the conclusion that the meetings had finally produced some progress toward putting some of their more advanced concepts into practice, all of which should please the Board up north.

And many of the pastors and missionaries, half joking and half serious, put their arms around each other and pretended to imitate Edward and Manuel in a three-legged race. No doubt about it — that meeting had brought the dawn of a new day!

Chapter Eight

We Three Will Conquer

(Epilogue)

On a Saturday afternoon a month later, Louis was once again in his office. Almost without realizing it, he began to whistle one of the hymns they had sung in annual meetings. And as he did so, Lila came in to ask, "Are you going to the Club today?"

"Absolutely. I haven't been able to go for several weeks — well, three at least — and I need some exercise if I am going to keep young. After all, with a wife as beautiful as mine, a man can't afford the luxury of letting himself get old too soon." Going over to Lila, he put his arms around her and gave her a thorough kiss. He had learned from his father that marriage is like a garden — it needs to be cared for and watered every day if it is going to produce flowers of happiness.

Then without further ado he went to his room to change clothes and get ready to go out. But just as he finished, he heard the doorbell ring. The cook went to answer and came running back to say that someone was looking for don Louis. Since she was new in the household, she was not acquainted with Louis's friends. However, Lila recognized the voice as Leonardo's and hurried to ask him to come in.

A twinge of resentment welled up in Louis's heart when he realized who had come. "What bad luck I'm having lately! Last Saturday I couldn't go because of that long interview with Joaquin — with no previous notice. The week before I had to attend to the delegates of the church at Barillas, and now today, Leonardo has to come! I'm tempted to give in this time. After all, I need to take care of my health, too." As he meditated, he heard Lila call to advise him that Leonardo wanted to see him.

It was obvious that Louis was not in the best humor when he came out to greet Leonardo, but he listened patiently as his visitor recited a lengthy tale of the problems which were troubling his church at the moment. When Leonardo finished, silence prevailed for several moments. Louis looked this way and that, and it seemed as though something extraordinary were bothering him. If he didn't go to the Club today, it would mean four straight weeks without a good workout, and furthermore it was a waste of money to maintain his membership in the Club if he never went there.

The more he thought about it, the more he convinced himself that Leonardo should solve his problem himself. He wiped his hands across his face and showed definite signs of indecision. Leonardo, meanwhile, took out a book to read while he made up his mind what to do. The book was titled *The Eternal Challenge of the Church* and the fact that he was reading it was a direct result of the annual meeting a month before.

He read a few lines, but could not help feeling somewhat uncomfortable as Louis continued to be silent. Discreetly he closed his eyes and began to pray silently, "Lord, Thou knowest that if this church is divided it will involve my ministry, my wife and children, Thy church, and the testimony of all of us. Thou hast said that the gates of hell shall not prevail against the church. Lord, give wisdom to don Louis so that he may advise me as to what I should do. I know Thou dost not want the work to suffer."

In that instant Louis knew the answer to his dilemma. As though upon a direct message from heaven, his mind flashed back to an experience he had faced as a young man, and how his pastor had taken him aside to read Acts 20:24. How well he knew that verse! "But none of these things move me, neither count I my life dear unto myself, so that I might finish my course with joy, and the ministry, which I have reveived of the Lord Jesus, to testify the gospel of the grace of God." The words hit him now like lightning. Still without uttering a sound, he prayed: "Father, first things must be first. Here I am, Lord. Do Thy will in me. Forgive my rebellion and all my faults. Help me to love Thee and put Thee first in all things."

His face suddenly lit up. Leonardo had been watching anxiously, and felt a tremendous surge of relief as he realized that Louis had just experienced some sort of spiritual breakthrough. "Thank you, Lord, for giving him the answer to my problem," thought Leonardo, and sighed deeply.

"Leonardo," Louis said a bit hesitantly, "I can't go with you now to see about this problem, because to be quite frank, I have to go to the Club." He waited a moment to study Leonardo's reaction. It was obvious that the pastor felt tremendously let down. He really did need help. Louis went on: "But . . . if you will give me a few moments, I think we can work something out. If you go with me to the Club I can excuse myself with the Ferrers, and then we can go together to visit these people who are involved in the problem. What do you say?"

"Fine!" Leonardo stood up smiling with relief. "Thanks to the Lord for your help."

Both men got into the car and started off down Progress Avenue, the wide boulevard which led to the Country Club but also passed a short distance from the church. As they drove along Leonardo remarked, "I think the three-legged race is going to be a big help for us, don't you?"

"Yes, I think you're right, but we mustn't forget what Agur said. Unless we are truly filled with the Holy Spirit we can't have a consuming passion for lost souls nor a true sense of responsibility. I see by the book you are reading that you are trying to put into practice some of the things that were mentioned the other day. I'm trying too — in fact, I've already been praying about some solution for the economic problems of you pastors. And just this morning I've taken another big step forward, I believe." Louis paused as he felt a mist well up in his eyes, and he moved the car to the curb and stopped. "What would you say if we just take a minute for a word of prayer?"

Leonardo nodded. Louis had trouble speaking for a moment but finally began to pray: "Father, if Thou wilt truly tie us together with Thy Holy Spirit, we will always triumph in every situation. The three of us can conquer the world, for Thine is the power, Thine is the Kingdom, and Thine is and shall be the glory for everything we do from now on. In Christ's name, Amen."

His companion echoed, "Yes, Lord, so be it."

Both of them seemed to hear again the familiar words of the Lord, when He said, "The Son of man came not to be ministered unto, but to minister, and to give his life a ransom for many" (Matthew 20:28).